DATE DUE

OCT 1 6 1995	
MAY 0 6 1997	

GAYLORD   PRINTED IN U.S.A.

BETWEEN

THE PLANETS

THE HARVARD BOOKS ON ASTRONOMY

Edited by

HARLOW SHAPLEY and BART J. BOK

ATOMS, STARS, AND NEBULAE
Leo Goldberg and Lawrence H. Aller

THE MILKY WAY
Bart J. Bok and Priscilla F. Bok

TELESCOPES AND ACCESSORIES
George Z. Dimitroff and James G. Baker

GALAXIES
Harlow Shapley

OUR SUN
Donald H. Menzel

THE STORY OF VARIABLE STARS
Leon Campbell and Luigi Jacchia

EARTH, MOON, AND PLANETS
Fred L. Whipple

STARS IN THE MAKING
Cecilia Payne-Gaposchkin

BETWEEN
THE PLANETS

Revised Edition

FLETCHER G. WATSON

HARVARD UNIVERSITY PRESS
Cambridge, Massachusetts
1956

Preface to the Revised Edition

In the years since the first edition of this little book appeared much has been learned about the various kinds of interplanetary materials. Increasingly fast cameras, sensitive and stable photoelectric cells, and the use of radio techniques have provided types of information not previously available.

During these years discussions of the origin of the solar system by von Weiszäcker, ter Haar, Spitzer, Kuiper, and Urey have involved a modified nebular hypothesis in which small particles play important roles. The available evidence about comets and meteor streams has been clarified by Whipple's "ice model" of comets. Both photographic and radar observations now allow not more than 1 percent of the meteors to have origins outside of the solar system. There have been other important advances in our knowledge. The whole area discussed here is rapidly growing both in significance and in technical detail.

In keeping with the plan of the initial edition an effort has been made in this revision to keep the technical details at a minimum while indicating broadly what is known, how this information may be fitted together, and where apparent inconsistencies remain. Because routine observations were severely interrupted between 1939 and 1946, some statistical tabulations have been retained from prewar observations.

Many have helped in this revision through comments and discussions. For advice on the radio chapter I am especially grateful to Drs. Peter Millman and Donald McKinley of the National Research Council of Canada and to Prof. A. C. B. Lovell of the Jodrell Bank Experimental Station in England. Dr. E. P. Henderson of the United States National Museum has supplied both constructive criticism and recent photographs of meteorites. Dr. Fred L. Whipple of the Harvard Observatory has continually encouraged and advised. To these and many others I express my sincere thanks. Despite their best advice the book may contain errors of fact or interpretation; these are the author's own responsibility.

I hope that the volume will stimulate further inquiry into some of the many complex problems presented by the bodies that move between the planets.

FLETCHER G. WATSON

April 27, 1955

CONTENTS

BETWEEN
THE PLANETS

Surveying the Solar System

Our solar system, of which the earth is a minor member, consists not only of the sun and nine planets, but also of thousands of small bodies which occasionally become far more spectacular than the brightest planet. A brilliant comet with its tenuous tail stretching across the sky; an asteroid swinging past the earth at a distance of a mere million miles; a flaming fireball abruptly floodlighting several states as it explodes, showering meteorites on the ground below — all dramatically reveal the usually inconspicuous small members of the solar system, occupants of the space between the planets.

Sometimes we think of the solar system as a close-knit organization of planets and their attendant satellites; yet the planets actually are only specks moving in a great void. If we imagine the sun as an orange 3 inches across, the earth shrinks to a mere pinhead 27 feet away. On this scale the distances of the planets from the sun and their sizes are shown in Table 1. Compared to the distances between them, the planets are minute. Yet interplanetary space is not empty, for it contains a wide assortment of wanderers which can be seen when they pass near the earth. We distinguish them as comets, asteroids, and meteors, but upon close inspection they show many characteristics in common. In this book we shall discuss these interplanetary wanderers and see what they are and to what extent they are related.

We find nearly all the little planets moving between the orbits of

1

Mars and Jupiter; many of them are very small, hardly larger than mountains whizzing around in space. Unlike them, thousands of comets, which are great clouds of gas and particles, move across the orbits of the planets. In the paths of comets are enormous swarms of

Table 1. A model of the solar system.

	Distance from the sun (ft)	Size
Sun		An orange
Mercury	10	A grain of sand
Venus	19	A pin-head
Earth	27	Another pin-head
Mars	41	Another grain of sand
Jupiter	140	A child's marble
Saturn	260	A pea
Uranus	510	A small pill
Neptune	800	Another pill
Pluto	1100	A third pin-head

particles which dash into our atmosphere, providing us with spectacular showers of shooting stars, or meteors. Larger solitary masses wandering through space become flaming fireballs when they rush through the earth's atmosphere. Fragments of the largest escape complete destruction in the air and fall to the earth as meteorites — the only solid material from space that we can scrutinize and examine in the laboratory. These bodies — the asteroids, comets, meteors, and meteorites — are the interplanetary wanderers, but to appreciate how they move, whence they came, and what they signify, we must be familiar with the planets and their motions.

How the Planets Move

At the center of this great assembly is the sun, which contains over 99 percent of all the material in the system. The planets all travel around the sun in the same direction and in paths that are nearly circular; as a result they cannot come together for neighborly visits. Seen from far above the earth's north pole the planets would appear like well-trained fireflies moving around the sun in a counterclockwise direction.

In addition to moving in the same direction all the planetary paths, or orbits, lie in nearly the same plane. The plane of the earth's motion is called the *ecliptic plane*, and the annual path of the sun, as seen from the moving earth, is called the *ecliptic*. The planetary system is a cosmic merry-go-round, in which the horses have nearly circular orbits, moving in the same direction and in nearly the same plane. However, the inner planets go around the sun much more quickly than the outer planets. The period of Mercury is only 88 days, while that of Pluto is 248 years.

Through its gravitational attraction the sun dictates how the planets and small bodies shall move. For ages astronomers tried in vain to predict accurately the positions of the planets at any future time. Finally in 1609 Kepler, using the extensive and accurate observations of Tycho Brahe, discovered that the orbits were not circles or combinations of circles, as had previously been supposed, but ellipses with the sun at one of the foci, at S in Fig. 1. Kepler also found how the planets move along their orbits, moving fastest when they are nearest the sun, at Q, the perihelion. From these relations Newton was able to establish the law of gravitation and to show how the pull of the sun made the planets move as they do.

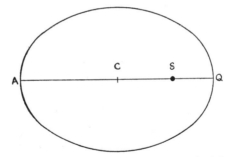

Fig. 1. *A typical ellipse. The size and shape are described by the semimajor axis,* CQ, *and the eccentricity,* CS/CQ.

Elliptic orbits can be of all shapes and sizes. As a measure of their size we take half the long axis, a, the distance CQ in Fig. 1. Within the solar system we compare all the orbital sizes to the earth's and take the distance between the sun and the earth as the astronomical unit, A.U. As a measure of the shape of an orbit we take the ratio CS/CQ, called the eccentricity, e. If the sun, S, is at the center, C, the eccentricity is zero and the orbit is a circle. If, however, the sun

3

is very near the point Q, the eccentricity is near one, the orbit is very long and narrow, and the aphelion, A, is far from the sun. The time required for a body to swing around its orbit is determined entirely by the size of the orbit. Kepler's third relation states that the period, P, expressed in years can be found from the equation $P^2 = a^3$, where a is half the long axis of the orbit in astronomical units. Thus Jupiter at 5.2 A.U. requires 11.9 years for a trip around the sun.

Near the end of the eighteenth century Bode was impressed by the regularity with which the planets were spaced and he devised the scheme shown in Table 2 for representing their distances. Al-

Table 2. Positions of planetary orbits according to Bode's law.

Planet	Distance from the sun (A.U.)	
	Predicted	Actual
Mercury	0.4	0.39
Venus	.7	.72
Earth	1.0	1.0
Mars	1.6	1.52
—	2.8	—
Jupiter	5.2	5.2
Saturn	10.0	9.5
Uranus	19.6	19.2
Neptune	38.8	30.1
Pluto	77.2	39.5

though this scheme gives reasonably satisfactory values through the distance of Uranus, it breaks down completely for Neptune and Pluto. Before the discovery of these two outer planets Bode's law appeared to be a very significant and fundamental relation. If it were, the position at 2.8 A.U. should contain an undiscovered planet. This belief was held so strongly that a thorough search for it was being organized when word came in 1801 that a little planet at this solar distance had been discovered. This planet and its companions, for it is not alone, may be the fragments of a planet spoiled in the making. In Chapters 2 and 3 we shall see how these little planets move and what they are.

Velocities and Orbits

The velocity with which a body moves along its orbit depends upon its distance from the sun and also upon the size and shape of its orbit. A body that flies away from the vicinity of the sun gradually slows down and then falls back toward the sun and sweeps around it to begin a new cycle. If by some magical process we could speed up a body as it moved away from the sun, it would go farther into space before turning back. A push of just the right amount would send the body into an orbit with an eccentricity of exactly one; this orbit is no longer an ellipse but is a parabola. At the earth's distance from the sun the velocity of a body moving in a parabola is 42.1 kilometers per second (26.1 miles per second) and any body moving that fast or faster cannot be a permanent member of the solar system.

The chances that a body will have exactly the parabolic velocity are almost zero. If it moves faster, the orbit is a hyperbola and has an eccentricity larger than one. In such a hyperbolic orbit, as in a parabolic one, a body moves off between the stars and never returns. We shall often mention parabolic orbits and the parabolic velocity, or the parabolic limit, which is the same thing, because they mark the dividing line between permanent members of the solar system and stray wanderers from interstellar space.

Although the planets move in nearly the same plane, comet paths are tilted or inclined at all angles. The angular tilt of an orbit compared to the ecliptic plane is called the *orbital inclination,* denoted by i. Some comets move up and down across the planetary orbits just as passengers on a Ferris wheel soar far above a carnival, then sweep down through the crowd. Figure 2 shows such an orbit; the comet comes up from the south of the plane of the earth's orbit, crosses the orbital plane (at the *ascending node*), and moves through the angle ω to perihelion.

If the planets were infinitesimal specks compared to the sun, they and the other members of the solar system would travel nicely along in the paths dictated by the sun. Jupiter and Saturn are, however, sizable bodies. Jupiter contains one thousandth as much material as the sun and Saturn contains a third as much as Jupiter. Consequently any body venturing into the vicinity of these planets will be attracted toward them by small but appreciable amounts. These planetary attractions, or perturbations, may pull the body forward, sideways, or backward in its orbit. Any such change in the direction of motion or in the velocity of a body alters its orbit and future path through space. To predict where a body will be, we must know

5

how close it can approach one of the planets and what happens when it does. The effects produced by the small planets like the earth and Mars are trivial, but Jupiter and Saturn do modify and even radically change the orbits of comets and asteroids that venture near.

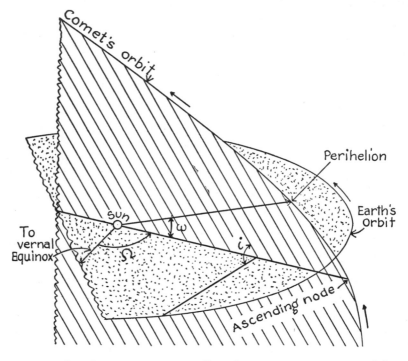

Fig. 2. *Angular elements of a comet orbit. This comet moves up from below the earth's orbital plane, crosses it in the direction of the ascending node Ω, and continues through the angle ω until it passes perihelion. The comet's plane is tilted by the angle i relative to the earth's plane.*

The Orbital Elements

The orbit of any body moving within the solar system can be described by only six quantities, called the orbital elements. These, and the symbols used to indicate them, are:

a, the semimajor axis of the orbit, which describes the size of the orbit and is expressed in astronomical units (A.U.);

e, the eccentricity, which describes the shape of the orbit;

i, the angular tilt of the orbital plane compared to the ecliptic plane;

Ω, the angular distance eastward along the ecliptic from the vernal equinox to the direction of the body's ascending node;

ω, the angular distance along the orbit from the ascending node to the direction of perihelion;

T, a date, usually the most recent, at which the body passed perihelion.

For parabolic orbits, *a* is infinite; hence, these orbits are described by the perihelion distance, *q*.

Temperatures

In many phases of the following discussion we shall be concerned about the temperature which a body has at certain distances from the sun. Since the source of heat is sunlight, the temperature T_r on the absolute scale (°K) at a given solar distance r will be given by the equation $T_r = T_1/\sqrt{r}$. Here T_1 is the temperature that a body will have at the earth's distance from the sun. The derivation of this equation is given in the Appendix.

What value to use for T_1 depends upon whether the body loses heat from its entire surface, or only from the sunlit side. If it is small and rotating, the body will have a fairly uniform temperature throughout of about 4°C, or 277°K, at the earth's solar distance. If, however, it is large or keeps one side toward the sun for long intervals, as the moon does, the temperature of the illuminated side may rise to 119°C, or 392°K, while the dark side is very cold. These two values for T_1 set the extreme limits of the possible temperatures for a solid, atmosphereless body. How the temperature may vary within the inner parts of the solar system is shown in Fig. 3.

Some of the bodies of interest move, however, not in nearly circular orbits, but in elongated orbits approaching parabolas. As a result, the time delays in heating and cooling may become important. Figure 4 presents curves for various perihelion distances, showing the number of days a body moving in a parabolic orbit will require to move from a given solar distance to perihelion.

From Figs. 3 and 4 we can obtain considerable information about

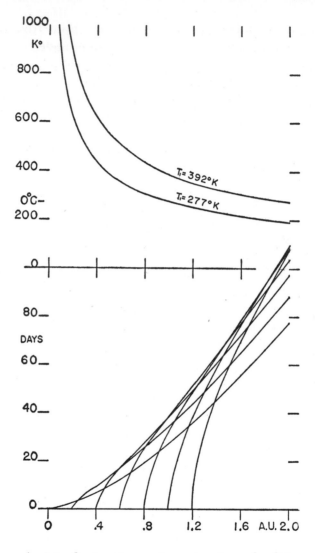

Fig. 3 (upper). *Interplanetary temperatures at various solar distances. The lower curve shows the temperature of a solid body that rotates with a short period. The upper curve shows the temperature of a body that keeps one side toward the sun for long intervals.*

Fig. 4 (lower). *The time interval in days from various solar distances to perihelion passage for bodies moving in parabolic orbits.*

a body moving through the inner parts of the solar system in a parabolic or near-parabolic orbit. Suppose we are interested in a body whose perihelion distance is, like Halley's Comet, near 0.6. How long did it require to move from a solar distance of 1.4, near the orbit of Mars, to perihelion? Also, how will the temperature of the body change during this time? Along the curve ending at solar distance 0.6 we trace back until it has a solar distance of 1.4; the vertical scale indicates that some 64 days will be required for the body to reach its perihelion position. From Fig. 3 above we find that at r = 1.4 A.U. the maximum temperature will be 320°K (47°C) while the minimum temperature will be 230°K (−43°C). At perihelion, r = 0.6 A.U., the maximum temperature will be 500°K (227°C) and the minimum temperature 360°K (87°C). If more precise values for these figures are desired, the formulas and values from which Figs. 3 and 4 were derived are presented in the Appendix.

The Metric System

Before considering the interplanetary material we should agree upon one last matter — the units we shall use in measuring distances and weights. Two distinctly different systems of measurement are now in common use in various parts of the world. We are most familiar with the English system, in which a mile contains 5280 feet, a foot 12 inches, a pound 16 ounces, etc. The other system is the much simpler metric system developed by the French and now in general use in continental Europe, as well as in most scientific work throughout the world. In the metric system each new unit is ten, a hundred, or a thousand times larger or smaller than the fundamental unit. We use this system for our money — there are 10 cents in a dime and 100 in a dollar. The basic unit of distance in the metric system is the meter, about one ten-millionth of the distance between the earth's equator and poles. A meter, 3.281 feet, slightly exceeds the familiar English yard of 3 feet. A kilometer, 3281 feet, is 1000 meters, while a centimeter is 0.01 meter, or 0.03281 feet. There are 2.54 centimeters in an inch. The fundamental unit of mass in this system is the gram, very nearly the mass of 1 cubic centimeter of water, approximately the contents of a thimble. A penny weighs 3 grams. A kilogram is 1000 grams, or 2.2 pounds, while a milligram is 0.001 gram. The metric system is so simple that throughout the remainder of this book we shall use it.

Now, fortified with this information about the solar system, the shapes and orientations of orbits, and the metric system, let us investigate the bodies that move between the planets.

☆
☆ 2 ☆

The Little Planets

Thousands of minor planets move around the sun, principally in the region between the orbits of Mars and Jupiter. These little bodies, when viewed through an average telescope, appear starlike and hence are customarily called asteroids. Despite their number, the asteroids receive relatively little popular attention, chiefly because they are faint; only one of them, Vesta, is on rare occasions visible to the unaided eye. Since they are faint, move slowly across the sky, and look like stars, the first discovery of an asteroid was long delayed.

The Discovery of Asteroids

On January 1, 1801, the first day of the nineteenth century, Piazzi at Palermo, Italy, was making routine observations necessary for his catalogue of star positions. When he repeated the observations on the next night, as he customarily did to check the accuracy of his work, he noticed that one of the stars was in a different position. On the third night a further motion was evident. Piazzi thought this moving object a comet, but certainly a peculiar comet since it looked like a star while the other comets he had seen were fuzzy. He watched it for six weeks; during the first two it moved slowly westward, then it stopped and returned eastward. Sudden illness

11

interrupted Piazzi's observations and when he was able to return to his telescope he could not find the moving star. He sent copies of his records to other observers, but the mails were very slow then and when the letters finally arrived the other astronomers searched in vain for a sight of the new object. Apparently it had been irretrievably lost.

Fortunately at this time Gauss was studying Newton's laws of motion and had derived a new method for the calculation of orbits from only a few observations. Piazzi's meager observations provided an ideal test for the new method. By it Gauss found that the orbit was similar to those of the planets and concluded that the new body was a little planet moving in the region between Mars and Jupiter. The orbit calculated by Gauss was so accurate that on December 31, 1801, exactly a year after it was first seen, the body was relocated just a moon's diameter from the predicted position. This discovery of a new planet, at first called Ceres Ferdinandea, but soon shortened to Ceres, was a major event in astronomy, but one soon to be duplicated.

In March 1802, while searching for Ceres, Olbers discovered another moving, starlike object, later named Pallas. Gauss found that it too moved between Mars and Jupiter with about the same period as Ceres. In 1804 a third, Juno, and in 1807 a fourth, Vesta, were found, but for nearly forty years thereafter no additional ones were discovered. Finally in 1845 a fifth, somewhat fainter, asteroid was added to the list and since then the number known has steadily increased. By 1891, 322 had been discovered by direct visual observation. Then Wolf, at Heidelberg, began to search for others by means of photography. As the asteroids move around the sun they gradually change their apparent positions among the stars. During a time exposure of an hour or more carefully guided on the stars, the asteroids move enough to make little trails, as in Plate 1, thereby revealing themselves.

After 1891 the rate of discovery increased greatly. Through the efforts of many observers using a variety of instruments several hundred new asteroids are now reported each year. Although the annual number of discoveries has been increasing, most of the new objects are observed only once. Figure 5 shows that the asteroids to which higher numbers have been assigned — that is, those which have been discovered more recently — are in general fainter than those discovered earlier.

The mere discovery of a new asteroid is of relatively small value, for we cannot predict its future position and locate it unless an orbit is computed. At least three accurate observations separated by several weeks are necessary if the position is to be predicted accurately for a year or more. At present only a small percentage of the

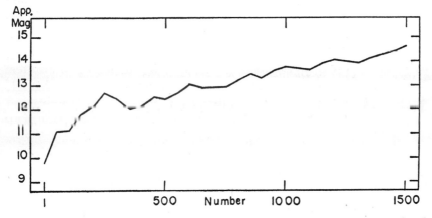

Fig. 5. Relation between average brightness and order of discovery of asteroids. The order of discovery of asteroids is indicated by the number assigned them.

newly discovered bodies are sufficiently well observed to permit the calculation of reliable orbits (Table 3). These asteroids and their orbits are numbered and entered in the register of asteroids, which now contains over 1500 entries. To each planet so recorded the discoverer may give a name. At first the names were taken from mythology. By custom those of goddesses, such as Ceres, Pallas, Juno, and Vesta, were used; but even the extensive roster of goddesses, major and minor, has been exhausted. Individuals, observatories, and cities in all parts of the earth are now commemorated in the heavens. With the exceptions of the Trojan group and a few others having unusual orbits, the names are put in the feminine form, as Piazzia and Pittsburghia.

Observers, both amateur and professional, in many countries contribute to the growing list of asteroids. Reinmuth at Heidelberg has to his credit a total of more than 1000 discoveries, of which some are rediscoveries and some single observations. About 200 of these have been numbered and entered in the register. Wolf's total of 582 discoveries is hardly half as large as Reinmuth's, but Wolf contributed 228 that received numbers.

How Asteroids Move

Before attempting to find out what kind of objects asteroids really are, we shall study how they move relative to the planets. Unlike the planets, the asteroids move in orbits that are appreciably elon-

Table 3. Distribution of asteroid discoveries by decades.

Years	Discovered	Numbered	Cumulative total numbered
1800–09	4	4	4
10–19	0	0	4
20–29	0	0	4
30–39	0	0	4
40–49	6	6	10
50–59	47	47	57
60–69	53	52	109
70–79	105	102	211
80–89	80	76	287
90–99	264	165	452
1900–09	776	213	665
10–19	788	249	914
20–29	1262	202	1116
30–39	2799	373	1489
40–49	—	76	1565

gated. A typical asteroid orbit appears in Fig. 6. Such an orbit is nearly a circle, but with the sun off center; between perihelion and aphelion the distance from the sun to the orbit varies by 30 percent. Hidalgo (944) is noted as having the largest orbit known. With a semimajor axis of 5.80 A.U. and an eccentricity of 0.656, it moves from perihelion at 2.0 A.U., not far beyond the orbit of Mars, to aphelion at 9.6 A.U., nearly the distance of Saturn. As a result of this great change in distance its brightness varies during its 13.9-year period from the tenth magnitude, at which it is readily observed, to the nineteenth magnitude, where it can barely be located with the largest telescopes.

The periods of the asteroid motions are distributed in a very irregular and interesting manner. According to Fig. 7, only a few require more than 6 or less than 3.5 years for a trip around the sun. In the distribution of periods there are several large gaps whose significance we shall later discuss in detail.

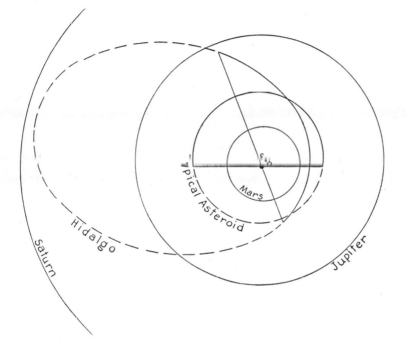

Fig. 6. Orbits of a typical asteroid and of Hidalgo. The broken-line portions of the asteroid orbits are below the plane of the earth's orbit. The orbit of a typical asteroid is tilted 10°, while that of Hidalgo is tilted 42.5°.

In their orbital eccentricities and inclinations, Figs. 8 and 9, the asteroids avoid exact similarity with the major planets. The average eccentricity of an orbit is 0.15 and the average inclination 10°. Only a few orbits lie near the plane of the earth's motion, while several are tilted at sizable angles. Despite the considerable range in inclination of their orbits, not one of the 1500 bodies moves around the sun in the direction opposite to the major planets; in this respect the asteroids are typical planets. Owing to the moderate inclinations of their orbits, the majority of asteroids are observed near the ecliptic. Any new one found far from the ecliptic is immediately subjected to close scrutiny, for its orbit may be highly inclined or the body quite near the earth.

In 1862 Newcomb noticed that the perihelia of asteroid orbits were concentrated on one side of the sun. While part of this arrangement may be due to seasonal influences affecting the likelihood of

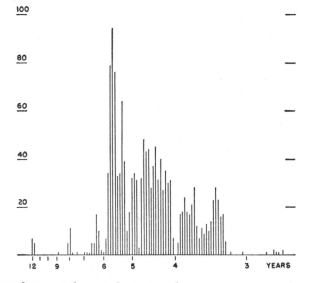

Fig. 7. Distribution of the periods of asteroids.

discovery, much of it is due to a tendency for the asteroid orbits to parallel Jupiter's, as shown by Fig. 10. The directions of the nodal points show, however, no similar clustering.

By comparing the orbital elements two at a time we can see to what extent their irregularities are associated. The pattern in Fig. 11 shows in detail how eccentricity is related to period. Of the long-period asteroids we might expect to discover only those having eccentric orbits that come in near the earth's orbit. Actually the reverse occurs, for, with the exception of Hidalgo, the eccentricities of the large orbits are consistently small. In a similar manner, Fig. 12 exhibits the relation between inclination and period. Here again the variation of the distribution reveals a striking interdependence; especially noticeable is the scarcity of large inclinations for periods less than 3.6 years. For the periods between 7 and 10 years the inclinations are all low, while for periods near 12 years the orbital tilts are widely scattered. Thus the shapes and orientations of the asteroid orbits depend upon their periods, which in turn measure rather accurately the closeness with which they approach the orbit of massive Jupiter.

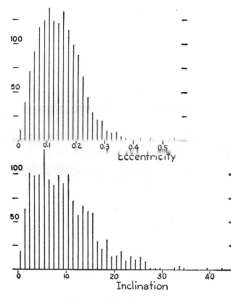

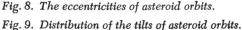

Fig. 8. *The eccentricities of asteroid orbits.*

Fig. 9. *Distribution of the tilts of asteroid orbits.*

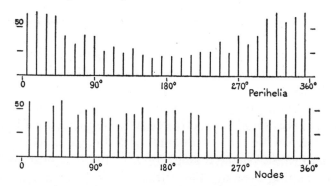

Fig. 10. *The orientation of asteroid orbits:* (upper) *the locations of the perihelion positions of 1183 asteroid orbits with respect to the perihelion of Jupiter's orbit, according to Fayet;* (lower) *the directions in which asteroid orbits cross the plane of the earth's orbit.*

17

Jupiter's Domination

The extent to which the asteroid orbits are controlled by Jupiter is most clearly demonstrated by the irregularities or gaps in the frequency of their periods (Fig. 7). The most conspicuous gaps occur at 5.95, 4.76, and 3.97 years — exactly one-half, two-fifths, and one-third the 11.9 year period of Jupiter. Other depressions in Fig. 7 mark orbits whose periods are one-fourth, one-fifth, three-fifths, and three-sevenths Jupiter's. Such orbits, in which the periods are exact

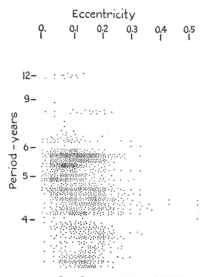

Fig. 11. Relation between period and eccentricity of 1492 asteroid orbits.

fractions of some larger period, are called resonant orbits, similar to the overtones of a musical note. If we strike a piano note, a properly tuned violin string will start to sing because it picks up the tone to which it is tuned. The violin string makes one vibration as each sound wave passes and is exactly ready to be pushed aside again by the next wave. Other notes do not find the violin ready or sympathetic and cannot make it sing. Another familiar example of resonance is pumping a swing. We always apply the push at the same part of the arc and in the same direction, thereby overcoming the tendency for the swing to die. Similarly with the motions of asteroids, those in tune or in resonance with Jupiter move in peculiar

18

ways. The steady monotonous pull of the great planet as they often pass near it in the same part of their path sets up rhythmic changes in the asteroid motions and eventually forces them into different orbits. The great singer Caruso knew well how devastating the effects of resonance could be. He would sing the natural tone of a glass goblet until it began to vibrate. As he sang louder and louder the goblet vibrated more and more violently until finally the ever-increasing vibrations shattered it.

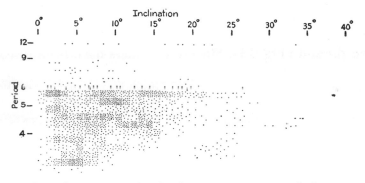

Fig. 12. Relation between period and inclination of 1492 asteroid orbits.

The mathematical theory of how and why such resonant motion produces the observed results is very complex and not completely worked out. According to the simplified investigations of Bessel and Newcomb, orbit groupings might be expected where gaps are observed. Later, Brown discussed more thoroughly the orbits with periods of 6 years. He found that neither their sizes nor their shapes could remain fixed and that periods within 25 days of the critical value must change rapidly. At any time few asteroids can have periods within this range. The position and size of this gap is confirmed by the observations. How and why groupings occur at periods of 8 and 9 years, where the orbits are remarkable for their low inclinations, remains a perplexing and unsolved problem.

Although the mathematical study of resonant motion is complicated and incomplete, the location of the gaps exactly at the resonant points leaves no doubt that they are formed through the accumulated effects of many Jovian perturbations. Certainly the present arrangement of these well-shuffled orbits can tell little or nothing about the positions and motions of the asteroids a few billion years ago when the solar system was newly formed.

Those asteroids having approximately the same period as Jupiter form an unusually interesting group, called the Trojans because those first discovered were named after Trojan heroes. Long ago the famous French astronomer Lagrange showed that if an asteroid was moving around the sun in the same orbit as a planet and was located so that the asteroid, the planet, and the sun were at the corners of an equilateral triangle, the asteroid's position with respect to the planet would not change. Many years later, in 1904, Wolf discovered an asteroid near one of the triangular positions with respect to Jupiter and the sun (Fig. 13). Since then others have been discovered

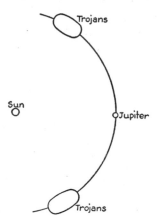

Fig. 13. *The Trojan asteroids. The Trojans are at Jupiter's distance from the sun, but 60° ahead of or behind that planet.*

and fifteen are known. Figures 11 and 12 show that the orbits of the Trojans, which have periods near 12 years, have small eccentricities and a wide range of inclinations.

Lagrange's ideal arrangement failed to consider the gravitational attraction of the other planets. As a consequence of the pull of Saturn, the Trojans occasionally wander far from their equilateral positions. Under certain conditions they could approach quite close to Jupiter, whereupon their orbits might be so radically changed that they might lose their membership in the group. Conversely, given just the proper circumstances, an asteroid might be captured by Jupiter and become a Trojan. Thus membership in this group is probably not permanent, but only one of long tenure. The best chances for capture seem to be from orbits with periods slightly greater than the critical values. Possibly there are asteroids other than Hidalgo in the zone between Jupiter and Saturn so far from the sun and so faint that they have escaped discovery.

All attempts to estimate the interval required for the asteroids and planets to reach their present orbital configurations have been unsatisfactory. Through the combination of recurring perturbations certain changes in the orbits are periodic and over long intervals of time vary within limits. Other changes are progressive, continually increasing with time, and after great intervals they produce important differences in the arrangement of the orbits. From observations covering at most a few thousand years the rates of only the short-period and the largest progressive changes can be accurately evaluated for the massive major planets, whose orbits change slowly. When we attempt to compute what their orbits were millions of years ago, the small uncertainties are multiplied by thousands and we can formulate no picture of the planetary arrangement more than a hundred million years ago. For the tiny asteroids that repeatedly pass near Jupiter our view into the past blurs more rapidly.

Hirayama undertook a search for indications of a common origin through the existence of "asteroid families." Among the orbital elements the great variety and the continual variation seem to mask any clues. Hirayama found, however, certain combinations of the orbital elements that would not change appreciably, despite the perturbations, during centuries. Searching among more than a thousand orbits he found nearly 200 which seemed to form five loose groups or families. Brouwer, in an extension of this investigation based on slightly different combinations of the orbital elements, confirmed Hirayama's five families and suspected 24 additional families among some 1500 orbits studied.

Size and Brightness

How bright an asteroid appears to us depends upon its size, upon its distances from the sun and the earth, and upon the angle at which it reflects the sunlight we see. A small body near the earth looks as bright and has the same chance of being discovered as a large body at the distance of Jupiter. Since nearly all the asteroids appear as points of light, we must estimate their sizes through their brightness. If we know their distances from the sun and the earth, we can compute what their brightnesses, or absolute magnitudes, would be at 1 A.U. from the sun and the earth and pick out the large bodies because they are brightest. The brightnesses are expressed in the scale of magnitudes, where numerically large magnitudes represent faint bodies, just as a sixth-magnitude star is fainter than one of the first magnitude. Two asteroids that differ in absolute magnitude by five have a hundredfold difference both in brightness and in surface area and consequently a tenfold difference in radius.

The earliest discoveries included the brightest bodies, which could be either small if near by or large if distant. In Fig. 14 the frequencies

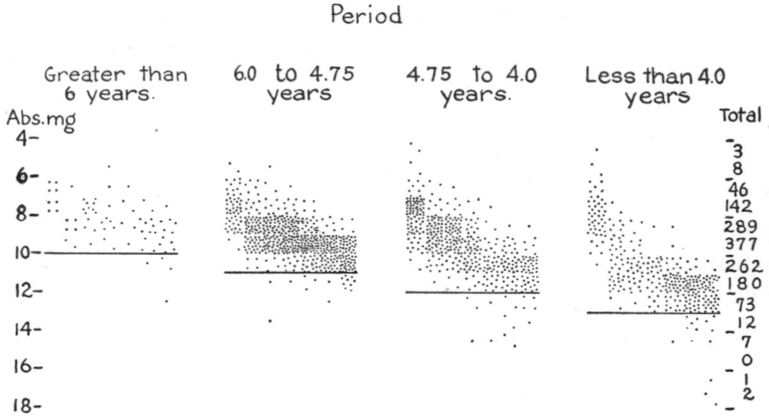

Fig. 14. The absolute magnitudes of 1400 asteroids. These magnitudes have been grouped according to period and order of discovery; early discoveries are at the left and recent ones at the right in each group. The distribution of the dots shows that we have discovered all the large asteroids of short period, but are still finding those of similar size far from the sun. The horizontal lines mark the 15th apparent magnitude when the asteroid is opposite the sun.

of absolute magnitudes are arranged according to intervals in the period and the order of discovery. For distant bodies having periods greater than 6 years discovery is still incomplete at absolute magnitude 8, while for periods less than 4 years incompleteness does not begin before absolute magnitude 11 or possibly 12.

From Fig. 14 we may estimate the number of small asteroids. For absolute magnitude 7 or less the total count of 199 is nearly complete over all periods. For the interval at eighth magnitude we may estimate the number, when complete, as about 330, and thus obtain a total of 530 with absolute magnitudes brighter than 9. Over these magnitudes the number of asteroids increases rapidly with faintness, approximately 2.7 times with each magnitude step. The number of faint asteroids yet to be discovered must be very large; with the increase factor 2.7 the number with absolute magnitudes between 9 and 10 awaiting cataloguing nearly equals the total now listed.

Another indication of the number of faint asteroids can be gained from photographs made with large telescopes. Baade, using the 100-inch reflector at the Mount Wilson Observatory, observed the number of asteroids within the zodiac and estimated that there should be 44,000 asteroids brighter than the nineteenth magnitude. From similar observations Hubble estimated the number as 30,000. The distribution of absolute magnitudes and solar distances leads us to expect as many as 80,000 brighter than the nineteenth photographic magnitude. On a single photograph made with the 48-inch Schmidt camera on Mount Palomar, Baade noted nearly 90 asteroid trails. Of these probably only four or five were catalogued. Certainly the number of small, faint asteroids is very great.

With the methods now in use, the derivation of precise orbits for all these faint asteroids will involve a great amount of labor. Already we are near the saturation point in this work, for only a few new orbits are derived each year, although hundreds of new bodies are discovered. In addition to the derivation of new orbits, all the old ones must continually be corrected for the perturbations produced by Jupiter and Saturn. There are, however, two interesting developments in computational technique. Elaborate electrical and electronic computing machines are being used to derive orbits rapidly. In one instance Herget, using such a machine, derived 14 new orbits in only 14 minutes. But because the numerous observations still require much effort to get and reduce prior to the computations, only a modest number of new orbits are derived each year. Another labor-saving method for the prediction of positions is offered by the technique tested at the Students' Observatory of the University of California. General perturbations — tabulated quantities which yield for any orbit the corrections necessary for the particular circumstances — have been investigated and found to yield positions sufficiently accurate for identification after several years. Since this is one goal of the calculations, we may expect the extensive use of general perturbations to reduce appreciably the effort necessary to keep account of these hundreds of bodies.

We have already seen how small bodies near the earth may be discovered while large bodies far away pass unnoticed. From Fig. 14 we can estimate the actual number of asteroids at various distances from the sun. Down to absolute magnitude 8 our discovery seems to be rather complete. In Table 4 we compare the numbers known in various zones. Apparently the asteroidal frequency is nearly symmetric about periods of 4.75 years. Five percent of the 199 large asteroids are Trojans, which suggests that 5 percent of all the asteroids may be Trojans.

Table 4. *Number of asteroids with absolute magnitudes brighter than 8.*

Period (yr)	Greater than 6	6–4.75	4.75–4.0	Less than 4.0
Number	27	72	72	28
Per cent	14	36	36	14

How much matter floats through the solar system in the form of asteroids can only be estimated. We can add up all the observed asteroids and see what they amount to, and we can compute what effect they would have on the planets if they totaled a certain amount. Using the latter method we find that if their total mass were a sixth of that of the earth they would produce observable changes in the motion of Mars. But since the predicted changes do not occur, the total mass of the asteroids must be much less than that of the earth and probably is less than that of the moon.

Asteroids That Pass Near the Earth

Several small asteroids that pass near the earth receive special attention. The first asteroid found to cross inside the orbit of Mars was Eros (433), discovered in 1898 by Witt at Berlin. Eros was immediately the center of much attention, since at the most favorable times it approaches within 23,000,000 kilometers of the earth. At this small distance it provides an accurate way to measure the distance between the earth and the sun, the astronomical unit. When

24

the distance to Eros is least, its position among the stars will differ by a whole minute of arc as seen from opposite sides of the earth. Precise measurements of the position at a given moment yield different results from different observatories, and since the distances between the observatories are known, the distance to Eros can be found in kilometers. From its orbit the distance can be computed in astronomical units, and a comparison of the two results gives the astronomical unit in kilometers. At present this unit is known within 0.1 percent, but a more accurate value would be welcomed because the astronomical unit is the fundamental yardstick involved in all our measurements of celestial distances.

In 1932 Delporte in Belgium discovered another closely approaching asteroid with an erratic orbit; in keeping with the erotic tradition it was named Amor (1221). Sufficient observations were obtained to give a reliable orbit and in 1940 Delporte reobserved the object only a few degrees from the predicted position. In the interval it had made three trips around the sun and was once again favorably situated near the earth. Albert (719) also has its perihelion in the zone between the earth and Mars, but it has never been seen since the time of discovery in 1911.

On April 27, 1932 Reinmuth at Heidelberg discovered a rapidly moving body, later named Apollo, which passed much nearer the earth than did either Eros or Amor. The least separation was a mere 3,000,000 kilometers — almost too close for comfort. From the few observations gathered before the little body faded from sight the orbit was computed and found to have a period of only 1.8 years and to pass inside the orbits of the earth and Venus. That Apollo was not a solitary vagabond thrown into such an orbit by a close approach to Mars was soon evident, for on February 12, 1936 Delporte and again on October 28, 1937 Reinmuth discovered other objects, now called Adonis and Hermes, having similar motions in rather eccentric orbits of low inclination. Adonis passed the earth at 1,500,000 kilometers, while Hermes came still closer, passing the earth at 800,000 kilometers, hardly more than twice the distance to the moon. The orbits of these three bodies are shown in Fig. 15.

On June 26, 1949 Baade found on a 1-hour photograph made with the 48-inch Schmidt camera at Mount Palomar an asteroid moving very rapidly; this photograph is shown as Plate 2. This tiny body, later named Icarus, is about 1.5 kilometers in diameter and makes a trip around the sun in only 409 days. The orbit is so eccentric, $e =$ 0.83, that at perihelion the body is only 28,000,000 kilometers from the sun, halfway between Mercury and the sun. At that distance its

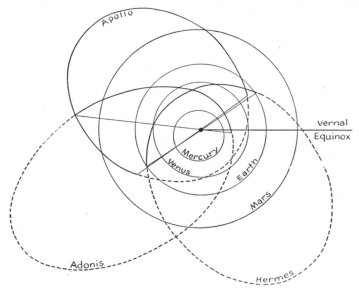

Fig. 15. *The orbits of Apollo, Adonis, and Hermes. All three move in orbits inclined only a few degrees to the earth's orbit; the broken-line portions of the asteroid orbits are below the plane of the earth's orbit.*

surface temperature, for a few days, must be above 500°C. Icarus was reobserved in August 1950 and probably can be kept under observation in the future when it is favorably situated near the earth.

Wirtanen, using the 20-inch refractor at the Lick Observatory, found in 1948 and 1950 other small asteroids that cross the earth's orbit and come to perihelion between our orbit and that of Venus. Neither these objects nor Icarus now approach the earth closer than 4 or 5 million kilometers. In Table 5 are listed the orbital elements for the asteroids known to cross the earth's orbit.

The recent discovery of this group of bodies is a great compliment to the alertness of modern observers and to their photographic technique. The difficulties of discovery and observation are shown by the fact that when the discovery of Hermes was telegraphed around the world many people attempted to photograph it, but not one succeeded, for it moved at such a rate that it was many degrees ahead of them. On October 30, 1937, when it shot past the earth, Hermes was of the eighth magnitude and moving 5 degrees an hour. In spite of its brightness no image could be found on several photographs known to cover its position. In 9 days it moved completely across the sky. The effect was much like that obtained by standing near the railroad tracks when the evening express roars past. The only observations available for the determinations of its orbit were from photographs taken for other purposes before the asteroid was discovered. Unfortunately, Adonis, Apollo, and Hermes were observed for such short times that their orbits are very uncertain. There is little hope that they will be observed again except by accident when they happen to pass near the earth during some future dash around the sun.

These little bodies, just 1 or 2 kilometers across, can be observed only when they are very near the earth. But to pass near the earth they must have orbits oriented in a very special manner, such that they cross the plane of the earth's motion when they are near the earth's distance from the sun. Thus the chances of discovering one of them is small and the few we know must represent several hundreds, possibly thousands, of tiny bodies with orbits like those in Table 5.

Table 5. *Orbits of asteroids crossing the earth's orbit.*

Name	Finder	Date	ω (deg)	Ω (deg)	i (deg)	e	a (A.U.)	q (A.U.)	P (yr)	Abs. mag.
Apollo	Reinmuth	1932	285	36	6	0.56	1.47	0.65	1.8	17
Adonis	Delporte	1936	39	353	1	.78	2.00	.44	2.5	18
Hermes	Reinmuth	1937	91	35	5	.48	1.29	.68	2.1	17
Icarus	Baade	1949	31	88	23	.83	1.08	.19	1.1	18
1948 EA	Wirtanen	1948	265	349	18	.61	2.26	.89	3.41	—
1948 OA	Wirtanen	1948	126	274	9	.44	1.38	.77	1.61	—
1950 DA	Wirtanen	1950	223	356	12	.51	1.69	.84	2.1	17
1951 RA	Wilson and Minkowski	1951	276	337	13	.34	1.24	.83	1.4	—

When these cosmic bullets swing past at a mere million kilometers we start worrying about the likelihood of collision. The earth's radius is only 6370 kilometers and the chances that a body scheduled to pass within a million kilometers will score a direct hit on the earth is about one in 30,000. Close approaches by these flying mountains are rare and the earth probably goes at least 100,000 years between collisions with them. Yet there may be myriads of still smaller bodies traveling in similar orbits. As we shall see in later chapters, sizable bodies do strike the earth every few thousand years, while millions of small particles dash into our atmosphere each day. In addition to these bodies that cross the earth's orbit, several more have been found which, like Eros and Amor, have less eccentric orbits and come to perihelion barely outside the earth's orbit.

☆

☆ **3** ☆

Whirling Fragments

What are asteroids? To answer this question, we must interpret the light they send us in every possible manner, for we cannot get a close view of them. As Plate 3 indicates, the light we receive from the asteroids is like that from the moon or any other cold solid mass revealed only by reflected sunlight. But small changes in the intensity and color of the light depend upon the nature and composition of the reflecting surfaces; from these subtle changes we must derive whatever information we can about the nature of the asteroids.

Through the largest telescopes experienced observers have seen the four brightest asteroids as tiny disks, but with the 200-inch telescope the diameters of 10 or 20 more may be detectable. Even when they are closest to the earth the disks are only a few tenths of a second of arc across, the size of a penny at 10 or 15 kilometers. Ceres, the largest asteroid, is 770 kilometers across, less than a fourth the diameter of the moon (Table 6). The small size of Vesta is surprising, for it has an absolute magnitude equal to that of Ceres. Evidently Vesta has an unusually high reflecting power, or albedo.

Because we cannot directly measure the sizes of the fainter and smaller asteroids, we must use their absolute magnitudes as an indication of size. Their reflecting powers differ, but we assume a representative value, that of Juno, and calculate, as in Table 7, what

Table 6. *Characteristics of the largest asteroids, Mercury, and the moon.*

Object	Diameter (km)	Absolute magnitude	p	q	Albedo
Ceres (1)	770	3.70	0.10	0.55	0.06
Pallas (2)	490	4.38	.13	.55	.07
Juno (3)	193	5.74	.22	.55	.12
Vesta (4)	386	3.50	.48	.55	.26
Mercury	5000	−0.88	.164	.42	.069
Moon	3476	0.40	.124	.584	.073

sizes correspond to various absolute magnitudes. The majority of catalogued asteroids, with absolute magnitudes of 8, 9, and 10, are less than 100 kilometers across. With this scale of sizes, we can see how large a body all the asteroids would make if they constituted a single mass. Bodies that differ by one in absolute magnitude differ in volume by a factor of four. But the number of small bodies seems to increase only 2.7 times with each magnitude, so for each magnitude interval the total mass is only $2.7 \times 0.25 = 0.68$ times that in the

Table 7. *Asteroid size and absolute magnitude.*

Absolute magnitude	5.0	10.0	15.0	20.0
Diameter (kilometers)	270	27	2.7	0.27

next brighter interval. Consequently, the faint asteroids add but a vanishingly small fraction to the total mass. By changing the brightnesses into sizes and summing, we find that all the asteroids put together would make a spherical body only about 1000 kilometers in diameter, or five times the diameter of Juno. The total mass of such a body would be less than one thousandth that of the earth, far too small to be detectable through its gravitational attraction on Mars.

Reflecting Powers of Asteroids

Since the asteroids are little solid bodies visible by reflected sunlight in the same way as the moon, we might well inquire into the peculiarities of moonlight. The most obvious lunar effect is its change with phase as it waxes and wanes each month. Careful measurements show that the quarter moon sends us only one-ninth as much light as the full moon. The full moon, directly opposite the sun in the sky, is a much better reflector than the quarter moon, and the moon's brightness decreases rapidly as the angle at which we see it changes from that of the full phase (Fig. 16). The asteroids far out in space treat light similarly, but, because they stay outside the orbit of Mars, they are always seen near the full phase; the largest departures

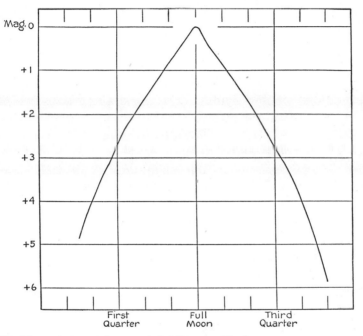

Fig. 16. The variation of the moon's brightness with phase.

are rarely more than 30° (Fig. 17). Yet after we allow for their changing solar and terrestrial distances this angle is sufficient to introduce a change of nearly a magnitude in their brightness.

The phase coefficient, that is, the rate of magnitude change with phase angle, depends upon the shape of the body, whether flat, spherical, or irregular, and upon the nature of its surface, whether smooth or pitted. Attempts to predict the phase coefficients of planets and asteroids on the basis of assumed shapes and surfaces have met with little success. Our best comparison is with the moon, which can be observed through almost all phases. Over the small phase angles at which they are observed the magnitudes of asteroids,

31

like that of the moon, change uniformly with the angle. The average value for 34 asteroids is 0.030 magnitude per degree. Over the same angles the coefficient for the moon is 0.028 and for Mercury 0.032. Mars and Venus, planets with atmospheres, have lower values, near 0.015. In 1933 Danjon at Strasbourg, through a study of earth light

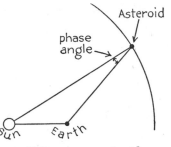

Fig. 17. The phase angle at which we see an asteroid.

reflected from the dark area of the crescent moon, found a value of 0.0156 for the earth's coefficient. This distinction between bodies with and without atmospheres places the asteroids among the members of our solar system not encased in protective layers of gas. This result is not surprising, for the asteroids are smaller than the moon, which itself is not massive enough to prevent an atmosphere from escaping.

Irrespective of what shapes the asteroids actually have, we can hardly conceive of them as having flat surfaces like those generally studied in laboratories. For this reason the fraction of light reflected by the asteroids is customarily called the *albedo*, while the term *reflectivity* is reserved for the description of flat surfaces. Any theoretical definition of the albedo is complicated by the variations of brightness with phase angle; the only practical definition is based upon observation. The fraction of the incident sunlight reflected toward the earth from an asteroid depends upon the reflectivity of its surface and upon the effects of the phase angle. If we denote the reflectivity by p, and the effects of phase angle by q, the value of the albedo is then the product pq. The value of p can be determined only for the large asteroids whose sizes we can observe (Table 6). Some of these asteroids are fairly dark, while others are very good reflectors.

The color of a material is often related to its chemical composition. For example, certain rocks containing iron oxides are gray or black, but upon heating they take up more oxygen and become rusty red. Through the study of colors of asteroids we hope to determine what terrestrial materials they resemble and whether they treat light in the same manner as meteorites, which may have been little asteroids before they encountered the earth.

There are three techniques by which we can measure the color of a star or an asteroid. They depend upon the fact that white light is really a mixture of all colors in definite proportions. With a prism we disperse the colors, spreading them out into a spectrum which may be permanently recorded upon photographic plates sensitive to wide ranges of color. By carefully comparing such spectrograms of asteroids and of stars like the sun we determine how nearly alike their light really is. Because the spectra are faint and this technique involves much careful work, the results are few and are limited to the brighter asteroids. Another index to the colors of fainter asteroids can be derived from direct photographs taken through blue and red color filters; a reddish body appears brighter in red light than it does in blue. By comparisons with stars whose colors are known the colors of asteroids can be determined rather accurately. For precise determinations of color, we turn to photoelectric techniques. Kuiper's photoelectric color measures show the asteroids to be the color of sunlight or slightly yellower. Although the differences are small, the asteroids do differ in color.

For comparison with the asteroids, only one study of rock colors, in which 47 materials were examined by Wilsing and Scheiner, is available. Although the results are not of high precision, they indicate what might be expected of almost any type of rock. Every specimen reflected more yellow light than blue and only three returned a fraction less red light than blue. These results indicate that asteroids are gray or brownish, like nearly all natural terrestrial materials.

Variable Asteroids

While observing Eros in 1900 von Oppolzer was astonished to find it changing greatly in brightness. Within 79 minutes it faded 1.5 magnitudes. During the next few hours it brightened to the original magnitude, only to wane again. A whole period, including two maximums and two minimums, required but 5 h 16 m. This unusual behavior attracted much attention, but the wonder soon increased as the great variation died away and within a few months disappeared. Thereafter when Eros came near the earth it was watched for a recurrence of the variation. Sometimes none was present, frequently it could be barely detected, but occasionally the extreme range appeared. Thus the mystery deepened.

Evidently the short-period variation results because Eros is rotating rapidly. The little mass may have light and dark hemispheres, like the rompers of a circus clown. Or it may be two small fragments of rock spinning around their common center of mass and sometimes eclipsing each other. A more reasonable model, which can be adapted to account for all the observations, makes Eros a long, thin, irregularly shaped body, like a rough brick, rotating about an axis nearly perpendicular to the greatest dimension. At times the earth and Eros are so situated that as it rotates we continually see only the top or bottom with no change in brightness. More frequently we are near its equatorial plane and see alternately part of the ends and sides as well as the top or bottom, with small variations in brightness. Occasionally the earth passes through the equatorial plane of Eros. Then ends and sides are alternately visible and the variations are greatest, as shown in Plate 4. Early in February 1938 the earth was due to pass through the equatorial plane of Eros and large variations were expected to appear. Observations during January and February of that year confirmed the expectations (Fig. 18), for the variation of Eros increased, as expected, to 1.5 magnitudes near the predicted time.

In 1931, when the distance between the earth and Eros was nearly the least possible, van den Bos and Finsen, experienced double-star observers at Johannesburg, observed its size and watched it rotate in the same direction as the planets. From the observed size, the length must be about 22 kilometers and the diameter 6 kilometers. Minor differences in the light variation between successive periods strongly suggest that the surface is not smooth, but quite irregular. We can best explain the behavior of Eros by considering it a whirling fragment, a spinning splinter.

After the large variations in brightness of Eros and their occurrence only at certain times had been discovered, other asteroids were watched for similar behavior. Of 74 studied photographically by Miss Harwood, 18 at one time or another definitely underwent appreciable variations with periods apparently ranging between 2 and 12 hours. Many of the others were suspected of similar behavior.

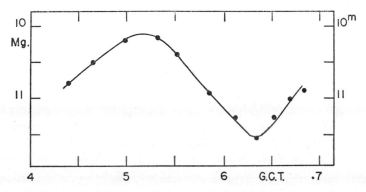

Fig. 18. *Light curve of Eros on February 5, 1938. Photoelectric observations by F. E. Roach and L. G. Stoddard at the Steward Observatory show Eros to have been varying by about 1.4 magnitudes. Photographic evidence of this variation appears in Plate 4.*

At the McDonald and Yerkes Observatories, Kuiper and his associates began in 1949 an extensive investigation of asteroids with photoelectric observations. They expected to find the majority of these bodies varying with periods exceeding 3 hours. Lengthy observing runs on 21 objects show that all but one do vary, with periods between 4 h 09 m and perhaps 18 hours, with no color change during the variation. Several, as shown in Figs. 19, 20, and 21, show two maximums of different brightness during the period. This is clear evidence that such a brightness change arises from the rotation of an irregularly shaped body. Other portions of this extensive observing program are intended to provide improved information on the numbers of faint asteroids.

Observations by Polarized Light

Reflected light, such as that from the planets and asteroids, differs from the incident sunlight in being partially polarized. By using Polaroid, or some similar material like Iceland-spar crystals, the degree of polarization can be measured; it depends strongly upon the phase angle at which the light is reflected and upon the nature of the reflecting surface. Lyot accurately measured the percentage of polarized light from the moon, the planets, Vesta, and many terrestrial materials. The moon, Mercury, and Vesta gave essentially

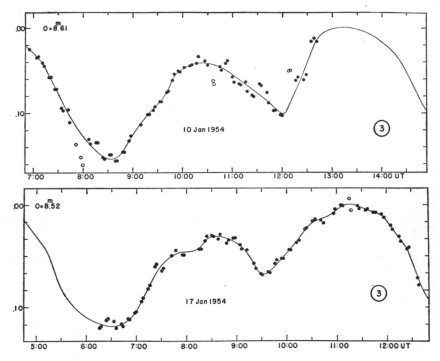

Fig. 19. Photoelectric light curve of Juno (3). From observations on several nights Miss I. Groeneveld and G. P. Kuiper at the McDonald and Yerkes Observatories derived a period of 7 hr 12.6 min. Although the range of variation is small, the light curve is what would be expected from an irregularly shaped spinning body. (Reproduced by courtesy of the Astrophysical Journal.)

the same results over small phase angles. We conclude once again that their surfaces are essentially similar in nature.

The nature of the moon's surface has been studied extensively by Lyot and by F. E. Wright. From polarization measurements, combined with our knowledge of how fast the moon's surface cools when it is eclipsed, they concluded that the moon is covered with a layer of some porous material similar to volcanic ash. We might not be surprised to find ash on the moon or Mercury, but tiny Vesta could hardly have supported volcanoes. Any porous material on it probably consists of dust and fragments resulting from the impact of meteors on the unprotected surface of the asteroid.

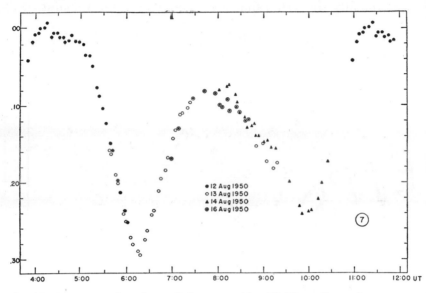

Fig. 20. *Composite photoelectric light curve of Iris (7). From observations on several nights in 1950 Miss Groeneveld and Kuiper derived a period of 7 hr 07 min. (Reproduced by courtesy of the* Astrophysical Journal.)

Origin of Asteroids

The title of this chapter summarizes our knowledge of the asteroids while suggesting a catastrophic origin for them. Short-period variations in brightness must mean that the asteroids are rotating and are spotted or irregularly shaped bodies. On a spotted body the light and dark areas generally differ not only in reflectivity but also in color. From photoelectric color measurements that were accurate to better than 0.01 magnitude per observation Kuiper found no color changes for any asteroid that he observed. At most, spottiness can play only a very minor role in producing the observed variations; irregularity in shape seems to be the principal cause. We conclude, then, that these little bodies are whirling fragments resulting from some celestial catastrophe or catastrophes.

Where and when such catastrophes took place, what was disrupted and how, are difficult questions to answer. The orbital arrangement of the asteroids suggests that possibly an interval of several hundred million years was required for establishing the present organization. It is frequently suggested that the asteroids are the remains of the

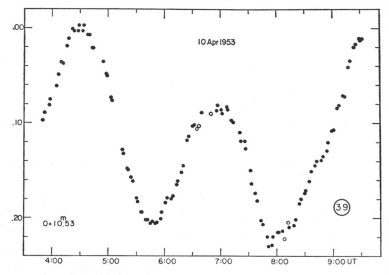

Fig. 21. Photoelectric light curve of Laetitia (39). From observations like this on several nights Miss Groeneveld and Kuiper derived a period of 5 hr 11 min. Similar light curves having different magnitudes at the two maxima and the two minima were found for other asteroids. (Reproduced by courtesy of the Astrophysical Journal.)

missing planet that, according to Bode's law, should be found in the zone between Mars and Jupiter. Some evidence, especially the probable large number of Trojans, hints that other asteroids exist in the zone between Jupiter and Saturn, or even farther out in the system.

Because some of the asteroids move in orbits like those of the short-period comets, a generic relation between them has been suggested. In the following chapters about comets and meteor streams we shall see that the comets and asteroids differ greatly in nature. The similarities noted are only orbital and might be anticipated, since the motions of asteroids and of short-period comets are both dominated by the perturbations produced by Jupiter.

Current discussions of the origin of the solar system are taking into account the possibility that two planets in what is now the asteroid belt collided. One planet having a size between that of Mars and the earth and a smaller one comparable to Ceres seem sufficient to satisfy the evidence; presumably a large fraction of the material would have been lost as a result of the collision. Kuiper has suggested that several, possibly as many as ten, little planets were formed. He suspects that the few larger asteroids are such original bodies and that only one or two have been shattered to form all the smaller asteroids. Despite the small size of such parent bodies, calculations indicate a reasonable chance for one or more pairs to have collided during the interval since the solar system was formed.

Because the major planets move in relatively stable orbits which have changed little over many millions of years, astronomers had assumed that the numerous asteroids and comets also moved along without mishap. Increasingly it appears that the small bodies are undergoing abrupt and drastic changes. Collisions involving asteroids, and possibly also comets, appear to have been inevitable. Thereafter the increasingly more numerous small parts must collide more often, resulting in further fragmentation and a general degrading of the sizes of the particles. The orbital and physical properties of meteorites, to be discussed in Chapters 9 and 10, seem consistent with their origin as asteroidal chips. Brouwer has suggested that each of the asteroidal families, first noted by Hirayama, arose from the shattering not long ago of a larger asteroid into many pieces which retain certain common orbital characteristics.

Any esimate of the interval since one or more planetlike parents were shattered into separate asteroids requires more evidence than is available. Our most definite information on the nature of such parental bodies comes from studies of the meteorites, but the interpretations lead to apparent contradictions.

☆
☆ 4 ☆.

Comets in Motion

From prehistoric times men have been awed by the appearance of great comets whose tails stretched far across the sky. For ages such comets were thought to be merely clouds in the atmosphere. Tycho Brahe found, however, that the comet of 1577 had the same position among the stars when seen from Prague and from his observatory on the island of Hveen in the Baltic Sea and was therefore more distant than the moon and a fit subject for real astronomical study.

Comets seemed to move across the sky mysteriously, in any direction at rapidly changing speeds. Attempting to account for such motions, Tycho assigned the comet of 1577 to a circular orbit outside that of Venus, while his pupil, Kepler, thought comets moved through space along straight lines. Halley finally solved the problem of their motion in his treatise on comets published in 1705. Using Newton's recently propounded theory of gravitation, Halley calculated orbits for 24 bright comets and found those of 1531, 1607, and 1682 to be strikingly similar. These he concluded·must be reappearances of the same comet moving around the sun with a period of 75 or 76 years. The variations of the period he correctly attributed to the attractions of the major planets. Halley predicted that the comet would reappear about 1758, but he did not live to see his bold prediction gloriously fulfilled.

By the time the comet was due the planetary attractions affecting the path could be calculated with some precision; Clairaut found they would delay its appearance by some 600 days. On Christmas Day 1758 an amateur astronomer located the comet once again nearing the sun after a trip that had carried it beyond the orbit of Neptune. Soon all the world was watching it swing past perihelion only a month from the date predicted by Clairaut. Thus Halley proved that at least some comets are permanent members of the solar system.

Through historical research it is now known that this comet, shown in Plate 5, has been observed and recorded many times during the past centuries. In the Chinese and Japanese annals it can be identified at every appearance except one since 240 B.C.

In 1818 Encke found that the faint comets observed in 1786, 1795, 1805, and 1818 were reappearances of the same comet, which was moving around the sun with a period of only 3.3 years. When Encke's comet was relocated in 1953 as a fuzzy speck of the twentieth magnitude, it was the forty-fifth return since discovery in 1786. This comet has the shortest period known, but many others have periods of less than 10 years.

Since a year may bring under observation as many as a dozen or more comets, some being recorded for the first time and others being return appearances of periodic comets, some identification scheme must be used to prevent confusion. When a comet is first observed, it is temporarily labeled according to the year of discovery, with a following letter to indicate its order among the year's discoveries; thus 1954i was the ninth discovery of 1954. Several years later the temporary listing is revised according to the order in which the comets passed perihelion, indicated by Roman numerals. Thus 1927c was later labeled 1927 VII, while 1935d became 1936 I.

Comets are also named for their discoverers, but by international agreement the names of only three independent or simultaneous discoverers can be assigned any comet. Comet 1954d is also known as Peltier-Kresak for two independent discoverers.

Short-period comets are always identified by the names of their discoverers. Thus 1951b, having a period near 7 years, is known as Arend-Rigaux. When the original orbit derived for a periodic comet was so indefinite that an accurate prediction of its return could

41

not be made, the name of a second or even third subsequent discoverer may be added. As examples we have comets Pons-Winnecke, Giacobini-Zinner and Tuttle-Giacobini-Kresak (1951f).

Discovery

Discovering comets is a great game that anyone can play. At present there is friendly rivalry between amateur and professional astronomers to see who can discover the greater number of new comets. The amateurs use visual telescopes and sweep the sky looking for fuzzy objects that move among the stars. When in 1954 the amateur variable-star observer and comet seeker Peltier in Ohio found a new comet of the ninth magnitude, it was his twelfth comet discovery! The professional astronomer can seldom spare the time for such sweeps, but relies upon his routine photographic patrol of the sky to record any comets which he may later find when examining the photographs. This technique would seem to give the professional a great advantage, but it has several limitations. Telescopes that can record faint comets usually take in only small areas of the sky and have little chance of hitting upon a comet, while cameras with wide fields usually have small lenses and do not record comets much fainter than the amateur can see. The first comet discovered through photography was found by Barnard in 1892; now more than half the discoveries are made in this way. The balance between the discoveries by amateurs and by profesisonals seem to be tipping in favor of the professional astronomer, for cameras that cover wide fields are now in use. Even so, the amateur who observes visually still has the advantage of being able to search where he will, while the professional examines photographs taken for other purposes in special regions of the sky. The twilight zone, which is rarely photographed, often contains comets that are near the sun and bright, or have moved up behind the sun in such a manner that we could not see them earlier. In 1947 and 1948 bright comets with tails several degrees long suddenly appeared near the sun and were easily visible to the unaided eye.

The chance that a comet will be discovered depends both upon its brightness and upon how it moves. Some may sneak up behind the sun and swing around it in such a manner that they cannot be seen against the bright sky above the sun at twilight. Others passing near the earth may be discovered readily even though they are much fainter. Our statistics are also influenced by the return of periodic comets whose anticipated positions and motion often allow them to be relocated while still extremely faint. Figure 22 presents the magnitudes at discovery of comets found between 1940 and 1949. The

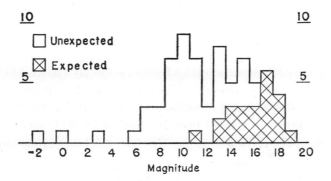

Fig. 22. Distribution of discovery magnitudes of comets during the decade 1940–1949. Returning comets, whose positions can be anticipated, are found at considerably fainter magnitudes than are new comets.

returning periodic comets, whose positions in the sky could be predicted, were found while still considerably fainter than the unexpected comets. Yet despite powerful telescopes that record comets between the fourteenth and twentieth magnitudes, a large number of comets were not discovered until between the seventh and twelfth magnitudes.

The years 1947 and 1948 were unusual, for each brought 13 comets under observation. The total for 1947 included five returning comets and two new ones of short period. During that year a total of 24 comets, including some from previous years, were under observation. In 1948 there were only two expected returns, but four new short-period comets were added. Both years included a bright comet — 1947 XII and the eclipse comet of 1948, both seen best from southern latitudes. Comet Johnson, 1948j, had the remarkably large perihelion distance of 4.7 A.U.; similarly comet Abell, 1955b, had a perihelion distance of 4.6 A.U.

The discovery of a comet is always an exciting event, for we immediately inquire: is it a new comet or an old friend returned after many years; will it become very bright and develop a long tail; will it pass near the earth? We cannot answer these questions until we determine the comet's position in space and how it is moving relative to the earth and the sun. To do this we require at least three observations separated by a day or two. Because any particular observatory may be under clouds during this time, astronomers in all parts of the world use a telegraphic code to spread the word of discovery and the first few observations. The Copenhagen Observatory in Denmark acts as a clearing house for Europe and Asia, while the Harvard Observatory acts for the Western Hemisphere. A typical message reads: "Comet Okabayasi 04117 October 18490 10073 22513 81101 20153 20056 76503 Hirose Stromgren," which meant: "Comet eleventh magnitude with nucleus discovered by Okabayasi. On October 4 [1940] at 18h 49.0m Greenwich Civil Time the position of the comet was right ascension 10h 07m 31.1s, declination 25° 13' 01", moving east 1m 53s, north 0° 56' each day. Message from Hirose [Tokyo], transmitted through Strömgren [Copenhagen]."

Experienced orbit computers who receive such a telegram and then two subsequent accurate observations of position begin the calculation of an orbit. If all goes well, the solution and a timetable of predicted positions for the next few weeks may be telegraphed to observers after 5 or 6 hours of work. Generally this preliminary orbit is assumed to be parabolic in shape, but sometimes the observations show that the orbit differs so much from parabolic that an elliptic orbit is derived at once. As additional observations are received, more accurate predictions of future positions are made. After the comet has finally disappeared and all the observations are available, some computer may take the entire set and derive the accurate *definitive* orbit.

Occasionally what appears to be a new comet can be identified with one seen long ago. In 1939 Rigollet found a comet that has since been identified with 1788 II discovered by Caroline Herschel; the period is 151 years. Similarly, a comet found in 1942 by Miss Oterma in Finland is a return of Stephan's comet, 1867 I, which has a period of 38.4 years but passed unobserved in 1905.

Two short-period comets also have probably been refound. Comet 1951f appears to be the same as 1858 III found by Tuttle and observed for only a month, then refound as 1907 III by Giacobini but observed for only ten days. Similarly, 1951k appears to be comet Wolf II, considered lost since 1925; it passed fairly close to Jupiter in 1948.

Types of Comet Orbits

The orbits generally fall into two rather distinct groups — those that are very nearly parabolic and those that are definitely elliptic and periodic. Just where the dividing line comes depends somewhat upon the accuracy of the observations available to the orbit computor, but the motion of a comet having a period of several hundred years is so nearly that of one moving in a parabola that the periods in these large orbits are very uncertain. Of new comets discovered since 1900, 48 were in 1941 still represented by parabolic orbits. Of the remaining 63 orbits 30 had eccentricities less than 0.990 and 33 had eccentricities greater than 0.990.

Of these 33 near-parabolic orbits, 15 had eccentricities just slightly greater than one, rarely exceeding 1.0005. If such eccentricities are taken at face value, we might conclude that the comets originated in interstellar space. But inasmuch as the sun moves rapidly through space, we should meet some comets head-on at high speeds and see them moving in decidedly hyperbolic orbits, yet no orbits are of this type. Perhaps the hyperbolic orbits in which the comets move near the sun are only temporarily hyperbolic. When we observe these comets, they are well within the orbit of Jupiter and to get there they must move in past the great planets and suffer their perturbations. Careful calculations by E. Strömgren and by others have evaluated the planetary attractions affecting more than two dozen such comets since they were near the distances of Neptune or Pluto from the sun, some 20 to 30 years before the comets were discovered. At those solar distances they were all moving in orbits that were calculated to be elliptic or so slightly hyperbolic that the difference is meaningless.

Furthermore, Sinding has pointed out that when a comet is visible near the sun we consider it to be moving under the sun's attraction and to be pulled sideways or outward by the planets, especially by Jupiter. When, however, a comet is far from the sun both Jupiter and the sun attract it in essentially the same direction. Under this slightly larger force, the eccentricity of the original orbit would be reduced. Sinding's general analysis predicted a decrease in eccentricity of 0.0005, which agrees well with the average of the actual changes computed individually for 20 comets. As yet there is no evidence that any comets originate between the stars; rather they all appear to be permanent members of the solar system.

Whether or not any of these comets continue to move in hyperbolic orbits and are lost to the solar system is not definite. Van Biesbroeck found that after comet Delavan, 1914 V, passed perihelion, its hyperbolic orbit gradually became elliptic, with a period of 2,000,000 years or less. Sinding's argument would lead us to expect that most, if not all, of such future orbits would be periodic under the total attraction of the solar system. If many comets are lost, the number of comets in the distant past must have been greater than at present. The only alternative to such a conclusion seems to be the assumption of some mechanism by which comets are being created within the solar system. But such possibilities cannot be considered satisfactorily until in the next chapter we discuss what a comet really is.

In Fig. 23 we see how the orbits of 100 parabolic comets are tilted. These far-flung members of the solar system show no regard for the

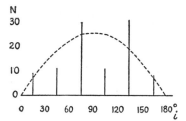

Fig. 23. *Inclinations of 100 near-parabolic comet orbits. The broken line represents a haphazard distribution.*

plane in which the planets move; half of them move in the same direction as the planets and half of them move in the opposite direction, called retrograde. Also the majority of them move in planes tilted nearly at right angles to the plane of the planetary motions. According to Fig. 24, 43 percent of them pass within the earth's orbit and 87 percent approach the sun within 2 A.U. We do observe a few, like 1948j and 1955b, that stay far from the sun; they must be very large comets, probably representing a multitude of others too faint to be discovered.

We can only guess what intervals these near-parabolic comets require for a trip around the sun. A comet that goes to the distance of the nearest star has a period of the order of a hundred million

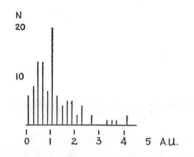

Fig. 24. Perihelion distances of near-parabolic comets. The majority pass inside or very near the earth's orbit, but some stay well outside.

years and, since the formation of the earth, must have made a score of trips around its vast orbit. If the orbit were much larger, the comet would be pulled away from the solar system by the attraction of some star passing near the sun. Comets having such long periods may not come near the inner part of the planetary system where we can see them. For all we know, there may be a great cometary cloud surrounding the solar system, a vast halo of which we are unaware.

The Periodic Comets

When we turn from the near-parabolic comets to those with periods less than 100 years we find increasing signs of organization. Of 40 comets observed at more than one apparition, only Halley's comet has an orbital inclination exceeding 90°. All the other periodic comets move in the same direction as the planets and 35 of the 40 have orbital planes tilted at less than 45° to the earth's.

Although the orbits of periodic comets are of different sizes and shapes, many have maximum solar distances near the solar distances of the four great planets. As a result rough groupings seem to exist in the cometary orbital sizes and periods. Comets with periods of 5 to 12 years go to near Jupiter's distance, of 13 to 18 years go to near

Saturn's distance, of about 28 years go to near Uranus' distance, and of 49 to 81 years go to near Neptune's distance. At one time these groupings were believed to have major significance. Russell showed, however, that because the cometary orbits are tilted the comets assigned to Saturn, Uranus, and Neptune actually passed closer to massive Jupiter than to the planet in whose group they were supposed to be. The short-period comets, with periods of 5 to 12 years, are, however, under the domination of Jupiter. In this group are 35 comets observed on two or more trips around the sun and about as many others seen only once. Two typical orbits of such short-period comets are shown in Fig. 25.

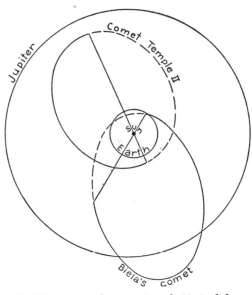

Fig. 25. *Orbits of Biela's comet and comet Temple II. Both have orbital inclinations of 12°. Biela's comet has a period of 6.6 yr while comet Temple II has a period of 5.2 yr.*

As indicated in Figs. 26, 27, and 28, the orbits of these comets have low inclinations and are moderately circular. Only a few of these short-period comets cross within the earth's orbit; some do not come inside the orbit of Mars. As shown by the direction of their ascending nodes, Ω, in Fig. 26b, the majority of these comets cross the plane of the earth's orbit in the same general direction from the sun. Since Jupiter crosses this plane 100° around from the vernal equinox, this is one further indication of the great planet's domination over these comets. One of their most revealing characteristics is the distribution of ω, which measures the angle between the long axis of the orbit and the line where its plane cuts through the plane of the earth's orbit. The values of ω cluster about 0° and 180°, which

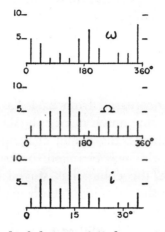

Fig. 26. Distribution of orbital elements of 40 short-period comets: (upper) orientation of the major axes; the majority of these axes lie close to the plane of the planetary orbits; (middle) directions of the ascending nodes; the majority cross the earth's orbit in the same general direction from the sun; (lower) distribution of inclinations; nearly all are less than 20°.

means that the long axes of the orbits lie very nearly in the plane of the ecliptic. When farthest from the sun, these comets are near the distance of Jupiter and about to cross the plane of its orbit. E. Strömgren emphasized this by pointing out that of 67 comets with

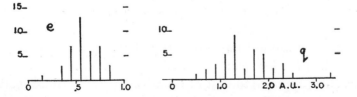

Fig. 27. Distribution of the eccentricities of 40 short-period comet orbits. The most common eccentricities are around 0.5; few orbits are nearly circular or very elongated.

Fig. 28. Distribution of perihelion distances of 40 short-period comets. Few of these comets pass within the earth's orbit.

periods less than 50 years 61 have either orbital inclinations less than 16° or values of ω within 16° of 0° or 180°, while 16 orbits meet both conditions. Of the 67 comets only two, both with periods greater than 10 years, are excluded if the limits for i or ω are raised to 22°. As a result these comets pass within 1 A.U. of Jupiter every few periods. The resulting perturbations are large and occasionally change the orbit drastically.

As an example, consider the orbit of comet Wolf I, discovered in 1884 and carefully investigated by Kamienski. By computing the comet's motion prior to discovery, he found that in 1875 the comet passed within 0.12 A.U. of Jupiter, when the perihelion distance of the earlier orbit was decreased from 2.54 A.U. to 1.59 A.U. In the new orbit the comet came much nearer the earth and was soon discovered. As Fig. 29 shows, the comet again passed near Jupiter in 1922, whereupon its orbit was changed to very nearly the orbit before 1875. Since 1922 the comet has stayed far from us and has seldom been brighter than the eighteenth magnitude. If it had not been discovered when it had the smaller perihelion distance, there is little chance that we would know of its existence.

The Capture Process

The short-period comets are perhaps not so well organized as the asteroids, yet they are unmistakably under the domination of Jupiter. The discussion of how they came to have such orbits leads us further into the way by which the perturbations of Jupiter affect their motions, gradually reducing their periods until they are completely dominated by the planet. This subservience came about by their being captured from a larger orbit at a time when by chance they passed near the great planet. What type of new orbit the comet will acquire depends upon the direction and speed at which it approaches Jupiter. Motion around the sun in the direction of the planets, with orbital inclination between 0 and 90°, is called *direct*; while motion in a direction opposite to that of the planets, with orbital inclination between 90° and 180°, is called *retrograde*. If the original orbit was a parabola in the plane of Jupiter's motion, we can find from Table 8 what type of orbit would result.

We need not worry greatly about the comets that are thrown into

Table 8. *Types of cometary orbits before and after close approach to Jupiter.*

	Original motion	New orbit
Large perihelion distance	{ Parallel to Jupiter	Ellipse, direct motion
	{ Opposite to Jupiter	Hyperbola, direct motion
Small perihelion distance	{ Toward the sun	Ellipse, retrograde motion
	{ Away from the sun	Hyperbola, direct motion

hyperbolic orbits, for they fly away from the solar system and constitute part of the cometary wastage. The most interesting result is for the comets originally moving nearly parallel to Jupiter: they are thrown into orbits of direct motion with short periods. Each time they come near Jupiter, they will again be moving parallel to the planet and will in general have their periods further decreased until

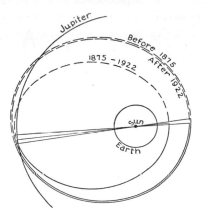

Fig. 29. *Orbits of comet Wolf I. The figure shows how this comet moved before it passed near Jupiter in 1875, between 1875 and 1922, and after passing near Jupiter again in 1922. The comet was discovered in 1884 during its second trip around the new orbit. Since 1922 it has remained far from the sun and has been extremely faint.*

they are firmly captured and become members of Jupiter's family. Any comets thrown into retrograde ellipses meet Jupiter head-on at the next close approach and are likely to be expelled from the solar system.

The rate at which Jupiter's family grows depends greatly upon how the comets move before being captured. If they move in parabolas turned at all angles to the planet's motion, Jupiter must change their motions greatly and can capture only a few that pass very near. H. A. Newton concluded that of every thousand million comets cross-

51

ing Jupiter's orbit in parabolas probably fewer than a thousand would be thrown into orbits of short period. Three-fourths of the 839 comets taking on periods less than 12 years would have direct motions, most of them at small inclinations. Since there are many short-period comets, we might conclude that myriads of comets moving in parabolas must be crossing Jupiter's orbit. But we cannot take too literally the computations, which assume that short periods were produced from parabolic orbits by a single close approach to Jupiter.

Changing Orbits

In their studies of this capture process the great French mathematicians Tisserand and Callandreau found that the difference between motion originally in a parabola and motion in a large ellipse allows a great diversity in the shape of the final orbit (Table 9).

Table 9. *Size and shape of short-period orbit after capture.*

Period after capture (yr)	Capture from			
	Parabola		Ellipse, period 130 yr	
	e_{max}	e_{min}	e_{max}	e_{min}
5.20	0.98	0.693	0.95	0.52
5.72	.97	.642	.93	.45
6.28	.96	.596	.91	.38
6.82	.94	.555	.89	.31
7.40	.93	.526	.87	.24

Most of the short-period comets undoubtedly come to their present orbits from ones of only slightly longer periods, as suggested by Tables 10 and 11, and the production of short-period orbits proceeds in many steps, each involving only a small change. Such a process acting on comets of moderate period is illustrated by comet Olbers. In 1889 it passed Jupiter at a distance of 1.5 A.U. and had its period reduced from 72.5 to 68.8 years, while the inclination decreased from 51° to 45°.

Among the periodic comets, especially those of short period, we find a continual state of change. Some move in past the earth for a few revolutions only to be whisked back into orbits that keep them far from the sun and unobservable. In Table 10 we see that many of the short-period comets were first observed only one or two periods after they passed Jupiter and had their orbits severely altered. Table 11 contains the former orbits of a few comets; before they approached Jupiter closely they moved with moderate periods and at such large perihelion distances that we could not discover them. To trace back the orbits of all short-period comets would be a laborious task, but undoubtedly they would exhibit large variations.

In addition to such large sudden changes the orbits of some comets show small progressive changes; comet Pons-Winnecke is a good example. This comet was first discovered by Pons in 1819, but was

Table 10. *Some short-period comets discovered soon after they passed near Jupiter.*

Comet	Near Jupiter	Discovered	Interval (yr)
Lexell	1767	1770	3
Brorsen	1842	1846	4
Wolf I	1875	1884	9
Brooks II	1886	1889	3
Faye	1841	1843	2
Finlay	1862	1886	24
Perrine	1888	1896	8
Swift	1886	1895	9
Whipple, 1933 IV	1922	1933	11
Ashbrook-Jackson, 1948i	1942	1948	6
Honda, 1948n	1935	1948	13
Johnson, 1949d	1932	1949	17
Shajn, 1949e	1947	1949	2

not seen again until 1858, when Winnecke rediscovered it. Since then it has been observed nearly every time it passed the sun at intervals of 6 years. Table 12 includes a sufficient number of orbits to show the gradual progressive changes that have occurred. Note how the tilt of the orbit has doubled, how the position at which it cuts the earth's orbital plane has moved around, and especially how q, the distance of closest approach to the sun, has increased, from 0.77 A.U., near the orbit of Venus, to 1.16 A.U., well outside the earth's orbit. If by chance the comet had not been observed from 1819 to 1951, we might not identify 1951c with 1819 III, but would consider them as two distinct comets. Then comet 1819 III would be listed as "lost."

While comet Pons-Winnecke was undergoing these large orbital variations, its motion was nearly in resonance with Jupiter's, the comet making two revolutions to one of Jupiter's. In Fig. 7 we found few asteroids having such resonant motion; the rapid changes of this comet's orbit illustrate the manner in which an asteroid taking on

Table 11. Effects of Jupiter's perturbations on some comet orbits.

Comet	Date	ω (deg)	Ω (deg)	i (deg)	e	a (A.U.)	q (A.U.)	P (yr)	Passed Jupiter Year	Passed Jupiter Distance (A.U.)
Lexell	1757	55	349	42.5	0.42	5.06	2.96	11.4	1767	0.023
	1770	224	133	1.6	.79	3.15	0.67	5.6		
	1779	341	179	18.2	.48	6.37	3.33	16.2	1779	0.004
Helfenzrieder,	1763	165	78	4.6	.82	2.86	0.50	4.85	1763	0.031
1766 II	1766	178	74	7.9	.85	2.71	0.40	4.40		
Brooks II	1883	2	187	6.5	.45	10.0	5.5	31.4	1886	0.001
	1889–1921	344	18	6.1	.47	3.68	1.95	7.07	1922	0.086
	1923	194	180	5.7	.50	3.61	1.80	6.86		
Wolf I	1875	158	208	29.5	.40	4.16	2.54	8.48	1875	0.08
	1884–1918	173	206	25.3	.56	3.59	1.59	6.80	1922	0.12
	1923	160	205	27.6	.41	4.10	2.42	8.33		
Comas Sola	1911	45	68	18.1	.52	4.46	2.15	9.43	1912	0.19
	1927	39	67	13.7	.58	4.17	1.77	8.53		
Schwassmann-Wachmann II	1921	335	127	0.7	.20	4.43	3.55	9.30	1926	0.18
	1929	357	126	3.7	.40	3.46	2.09	6.42		
Whipple, 1933 IV	1920	149	200	8.5	.35	4.74	3.94	10.3	1922	0.26
	1934	191	189	10.2	.17	3.83	2.50	7.5		

resonant motion is speedily shifted into a different orbit. Changes of this sort are of such a size that we cannot keep account of the comet unless it is observed frequently. If it sneaks around behind the sun and misses being observed at several consecutive perihelion passages, we may have difficulty in predicting where to search when it is next due near the sun. Looking for a needle in a haystack is simple compared to locating a faint comet whose position is unknown.

Vanishing Comets

A sizable number of periodic comets have been observed only once or twice and then not found again when subsequently due at perihelion. In some cases the predicted positions were too inaccurate to be dependable; at other times little attempt was made to locate the comet because other endeavors distracted the observers. Yet in a few cases careful observations were made according to a reliable timetable, but no comet was found. When near the sun and exposed to strong radiation, all comets probably lose material and hence become fainter. But in addition to this gradual wasting away,

Table 12. Orbits of Comet Pons-Winnecke.

Identification	ω (deg)	Ω (deg)	i (deg)	e	q (A.U.)	P (yr)
1819 III	162	113	10.7	0.755	0.774	5.62
1858 II	162	113	10.8	.755	.764	5.56
1886 VI	172	104	14.5	.726	.886	5.80
1898 II	173	101	17.0	.715	.924	5.88
1927 VII	170	98	18.9	.685	1.04	5.99
1951c	170	94	21.7	.654	1.16	6.12

some comets have disintegrated while under observation. Although the process is disastrous to the comet, it makes the comet famous and simultaneously tells us much about its structure.

The most notable example of such disintegration is Biela's comet, first observed in 1772. It was observed again in 1815 and in 1826 when its periodic orbit was derived. Thereafter it appeared on schedule in 1832, but in 1839 it stayed near the sun in the sky and was not located. In 1845, after an absence of 13 years, it appeared much as it had before. In the middle of January 1846 several observers were astonished to find two comets where one had been a few nights previously. These two comets moved along together, changing in brightness in a singular manner, first one then the other being the brighter. Calculating back the relative positions of the two components, Hubbard found that the comet probably split more than a year before it was observed as double, but by chance one component was hidden behind the other until they were near the earth.

Naturally the return of this double comet in 1852 was eagerly awaited. It came on schedule and had only one peculiarity — one component was bright and the other faint. In 1859, as in 1839, it stayed nearly in line with the sun and passed unobserved. In 1865 it should again have been favorably placed for observation, but it could not be found and has never been seen since. The general disintegration that developed between 1832 and 1845 probably continued and the comet became too scattered and faint to be visible. We have more evidence about what happened to Biela's comet, but that comes in Chapter 7 where we discuss meteor showers.

The behavior of Biela's comet is not an isolated example. Taylor's comet, which divided in 1916 and has not been seen again, split when it was nearest the sun. Similarly Ensor's comet, 1926 III, which had a parabolic orbit, was of the eighth magnitude when discovered two months before perihelion passage at 0.33 A.U. Had it brightened like a typical comet, it would have become visible to the unaided eye. Instead, as it neared perihelion it spread out, became very diffuse, and soon disappeared. In 1913, as comet Westfal, having a period of 61 years, moved toward perihelion at 1.25 A.U., it became very diffuse and faded by 10 magnitudes in 6 weeks. Similarly, comet Perrine, 1897 III, faded and vanished as it moved toward perihelion. These comets and others have faded and disappeared, perhaps actually melted away, as they approached the sun.

A wide variety of mechanisms and forces operate to disperse the material of a comet. These mechanisms include continual loss of material into the tail, collisions between the comet and other particles moving between the planets, and electrical repulsion resulting from charges built up by photoelectric action of sunlight and by cosmic rays. This variety of disintegrating mechanisms is offset, so far as we can imagine, only by whatever cohesive forces exist within the solid material of a comet and by the gravitational attraction of this mass upon any fragments that come loose. As the comets are of low mass and emit tail-forming material, there is little wonder that they fade away. The heating effects of sunlight near perihelion plus the other distintegrating forces seem to release particles that move independently. Through planetary perturbations and perhaps initial ejection they take on slightly different orbits and run ahead of or behind the main mass as swarms of dark particles.

That comets do possess some cohesive core is a necessary conclusion based on the past history of comet Brooks II. In 1886 it passed very close to Jupiter, going between the satellites and nearly grazing the surface of the planet. Had it been a loose assemblage of separate particles, the gravitational attraction of the great planet would have torn the cloud to shreds. Yet the comet is still observable and appeared on schedule in 1946.

☆

☆ 5 ☆

Anatomy of a Comet

A bright comet appears as a fuzzy spot in the sky with a tail stretching out like a plume of smoke. As it moves toward the sun and perihelion before starting its journey out into cold interplanetary space the comet rapidly goes through a variety of changes, as shown in Plate 7, increasing in brightness, growing a tail, and sometimes showing remarkable variations of structure within a few hours. No two comets behave exactly alike and even those that return period- ically rarely behave the same at successive appearances. Such changes tell us immediately that comets are unique among the popu- lation of the solar system, for when near the sun they are great clouds of gas surrounding some solid material (Fig. 30).

Through a telescope we see the head of a comet as two distinct parts: a small sharp nucleus embedded in a large nebulous coma. As we focus our attention upon the nucleus and examine it under higher and higher magnification its size does not increase — it always looks like a star seen through a fog. Perhaps there is no real nucleus in some comets, but just a sharp increase in brightness which we see as a central point of light. Indeed, some comets have been without a visible nucleus, merely appearing as a large nebulous patch of light.

The coma of a comet is a large luminous envelope, brightest around the nucleus and gradually fading off toward the edges until it can no longer be seen. Within the comae of a few comets, usually

57

the brightest and most active, are sharp gradations of light surrounding the nucleus (Plates 8 and 9). These envelopes expand through the coma like a series of waves, eventually vanishing. The heads of comets are usually tens of thousands of kilometers across, rivaling the size of Jupiter; a few have even exceeded the volume of the sun.

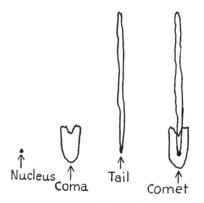

Fig. 30. The structure of a comet. The light of a comet comes from three different sources: the nucleus reflects sunlight, the coma emits light from short-lived molecules, and the tail emits light from less fragile molecules.

Comet tails point away from the sun, as suggested by Fig. 31. When a comet moves toward the sun, the tail trails behind; as it moves away from the sun, it goes tail first. Those of us who marvel at the beauty of a great comet's tail stretching across the sky are fortunate to live on the earth and not on Jupiter or one of the other planets at the outskirts of the solar system, for comets very rarely grow their tails until they have passed inside the orbit of Mars. At greater distances from the sun a comet is all coma, a polliwog with a stubby tail a few hundred thousand kilometers long. In a typical case the real tail does not begin to grow until the comet is about the earth's distance from the sun. Then the activity begins and the tail shoots out at the rate of a million kilometers per day until it may be fifty to a hundred million kilometers long. The maximum tail length on record is that of the great comet of 1843; its tail stretched into space 300,000,000 kilometers, twice the distance from the earth to the sun. In 1910 the tail of Halley's comet grew to 50,000,000 kilometers by the time it passed perihelion, and continued to grow for several weeks thereafter, reaching a maximum length of 150,000,-

000 kilometers. The apparent length of such a tail depends upon the angle at which we see it. When in 1910 the earth passed near or through the tail of Halley's comet it stretched 150°, nearly across the entire sky. Although a few weeks later the tail was actually longer, we saw it more nearly end-on, so that it covered only 50°.

Formation of Comet Tails

As we see a comet's tail in the sky it always points away from the sun and must actually extend away from the sun, like a plume of smoke floating down wind. Some force emanating from the sun

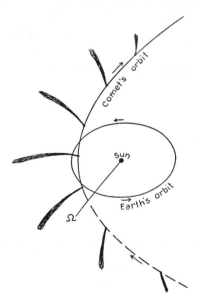

Fig. 31. A comet's tail points away from the sun.

was long recognized as the cause, but the force was not identified until the beginning of this century, when physicists showed that light exerts a pressure on tiny particles and actually does blow them away. This outward force is extremely small and affects only minute dust particles a few microns (millionths of a meter) in diameter and molecules of gas. As it pushes on these bits of matter, it partly offsets or even exceeds the gravitational attraction of the sun. When a comet nears the sun the amount of sunlight passing through it increases at exactly the same rate as the pull of the sun increases, so the relation between attraction and repulsion does not change.

Another type of effect may be equally or even more important in the formation of comet tails. Biermann has called attention to the repulsion effects resulting from corpuscular radiation from the sun. Charged particles, especially protons, which are electrically charged hydrogen atoms, are known to stream from the sun in large quantities. They are the principal cause of the earth's aurora. When these charged particles hit a comet, they will interact with the gases in the coma and drive them out of the comet in the direction away from the sun.

If a comet moved directly toward the sun, its tail would point directly away from the sun, but comets move around the sun and this motion spreads their tails over curved paths. When the material rushes out at tremendous speed, the tail appears almost straight; but when it floats away leisurely, the tail is decidedly curved. Often a comet has several tails of different curvature showing at the same time, as did comet 1910 I (Plate 10).

When a tail contains small knots or irregularities we can identify them on successive days and measure their speed, thereby evaluating the forces propelling them away from the sun. Usually the outward force is only a few times the sun's gravitational attraction, but Orlow, Eddington, and Cherrington all found that forces more than a thousand times the sun's gravitation acted upon comet Morehouse, 1908 III (Plates 11 and 12). This comet was one of the most active ever seen. Within a few days it radically changed its appearance and often showed great clouds or jets of material moving millions of kilometers along the tail in only a few hours.

All the material in a comet's tail is moving in hyperbolic orbits and is lost to the comet. Obviously no comet can keep producing a limitless number of tails, even though each contains only a small quantity of material. We are not surprised to find that the comets of short period that pass inside the earth's orbit now grow no appreciable tails. Their supply of tail-stuff has been exhausted during their many past trips around the sun. Halley's comet continues to grow elegant tails after 30 observed trips around the sun, but even it is suspected of having faded somewhat during the past thousand years.

A Comet's Brightness

As comets approach the sun they brighten rapidly, but at various rates. Consequently we have difficulties in predicting how bright any particular comet will become when nearest the sun. An asteroid that reflects sunlight brightens according to the amount of sunlight falling on it, but comets brighten more rapidly. If, for instance, the solar distance of an asteroid and a comet are halved, the asteroid becomes four times as bright, but a typical comet will become 10 times as bright and some comets even become 50 times as luminous.

Vsessviatsky has attempted to intercompare the intrinsic brightness of comets by computing for them cometary absolute magnitudes — how bright they would be at 1 A.U. from the sun and the earth. In the left-hand part of Fig. 32 is shown the distribution of

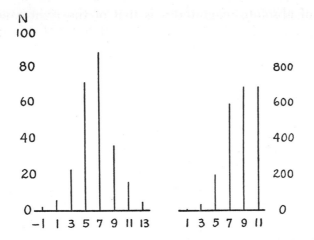

Fig. 32. The absolute magnitudes of near-parabolic comets: (left) the observed distribution; (right) the actual distribution, according to Bourgeois and Cox, in which faint comets are extremely abundant.

absolute magnitudes he derived for near-parabolic comets, and we notice that they have a great diversity. The short-period comets are among the faintest known, generally having absolute magnitudes between 8 and 14. We have already seen that some comets break up and vanish. Probably the short-period comets cannot remain visible for more than a few thousand years. Yet we shall find evidence that

Encke's comet has been moving in essentially its present orbit for perhaps 5000 years, during which time it has made more than 1000 approaches within 0.4 A.U. of the sun. Although one of the faintest comets known, it is still visible.

Perhaps the greatest comet ever observed was that of 1729, which never approached within 4 A.U. of the sun yet was visible to the unaided eye. At the same solar distance Halley's comet was ten magnitudes fainter. The great comet of 1729 had an absolue magnitude near -6, completely outside the limits of Fig. 32. The fact that it could be observed with the unaided eye at that great solar distance while many other comets passing near the earth can barely be seen through large telescopes emphasizes our difficulties in discovering and properly counting the intrinsically faint comets. Bourgeois and Cox have computed what chances we have of discovering comets of various absolute magnitudes and they conclude that the actual distribution of absolute magnitudes is that of the right-hand part of Fig. 32. Even this distribution is provisional, but it clearly shows that among the comets as well as the asteroids we are merely skimming the bright objects from the total. How many comets belong to the solar system we can only guess, for we have no idea how many come to perihelion at the distance of Jupiter, Saturn, and Uranus, or how many have extremely long-period orbits, bringing them among the planets at tremendous intervals. Yet any reasonable guess must make the total, bright and faint, among the hundreds of thousands.

Through an extensive investigation of 45 comets Bobrovnikoff has added considerably to our knowledge of how comets change in brightness. By allowing for the differences between observations made with telescopes, binoculars, and the unaided eye, he reduced all the observations to a single magnitude system. Analysis of more than 4000 observations revealed no effect of phase angle or any average difference of brightness variations before and after perihelion passage. Bobrovnikoff found that the average dependence of cometary brightness upon solar distance changed with the 3.3 power of the solar distance. However, the idiosyncracies of comets were apparent, for some were brighter when far from the sun than when near it, while others brightened more rapidly than the average as they neared the sun. Two-thirds of these comets were suspected of periodic variation in brightness, and further study revealed periods of between 12 and 600 days. Such periodic variation is presumably associated with rotation of the cometary nucleus.

The difficulties of determining the brightness of a comet are great because the comet has no definite edge; the outer parts just get fainter and fainter. This is illustrated by lines of equal brightness, or isophotes, determined by Watson from a series of photographs of comet Cunningham, 1941 I (Plate 13). Even on the exposure of 1 minute the tiny central nucleus was too black to be measured with the microdensitometer. These isophotes show more light coming from the large but faint outer region of the comet than from the central coma. This emphasizes the uncertainties encountered in the estimation of cometary magnitudes.

Some of the difficulties involved in predicting the brightness of comets are well illustrated by the behaviors of comet Holmes and of comet Schwassmann-Wachmann I. On November 6, 1892, Holmes discovered a comet faintly visible to the unaided eye. According to its orbit the comet should have been bright and well placed for discovery throughout the previous two months, yet it had escaped detection. In January 1893, after two weeks of cloudy weather, Barnard hoped to have one last look at it before it faded beyond the limit of his telescope. Instead of seeing a very faint fuzzy area, he found it bright, appearing as a star of the eighth magnitude. During successive nights it increased in size, regaining an appearance similar to that at its discovery. Presumably it had been faint when nearest the sun, then flared up and was soon found. In 1899 it was again visible to the unaided eye, but in 1906 it was very faint. Since then it has not been seen.

Comet Schwassmann-Wachmann I has the most peculiar orbit known, for it has an eccentricity of only 0.142 and an average distance of 6.43 A.U. from the sun. As a result the comet remains in the region between Jupiter and Saturn (Fig. 33), coming to perihelion at 5.51 A.U. and to aphelion at 7.34 A.U. Generally it is near the eighteenth magnitude and would have passed unknown except for its peculiar habit of flaring up suddenly, becoming a hundred times brighter within a few days. Such flares have occurred several times. The comet brightens very quickly; in 1934 on March 10 it was of the eighteenth and on March 14 of the thirteenth magnitude. Within a few weeks it faded away to its original brightness. Several other abrupt brightenings have been observed, such as those in November 1947, in January 1949, and in April 1952, but these outbursts do not seem to be periodic. Mayall at the Lick Observatory has obtained several spectrograms of this comet when it has been brightest. These show no bright bands or lines, but seem to be pure reflections of sunlight, showing even the *H* and *K* lines and the *G* band in absorption. What causes such sudden increases in reflecting power is a mystery. Our observations would be less confusing were other comets to show similar flares at comparable distances from the sun, but they do not. Comet Oterma, discovered in 1943, like comet Schwassmann-Wachmann I, has a nearly circular orbit, $e = 0.144$, but remains inside the orbit of Jupiter, in the asteroid zone. This comet can be observed each year and might be expected to behave like its more distant counterpart, but no irregularities in the brightness of comet Oterma have been noticed.

The Mass of a Comet

The total quantity of matter in a comet cannot be measured accurately, for it has too little mass to exert any measurable pull upon any planet it approaches. Lexell's comet passed so close to the earth in 1770 that our meager pull changed its period by several days, yet no observable changes in the motion or rotation of the earth resulted. This comet must have had a mass less than one ten-thousandth that of the earth. Yet this would be a sizable amount of material, nearly a million million million tons. The real mass of even a great comet is, however, probably much below this value, possibly only a million million tons.

If this amount of material is distributed over a volume equal to that of Jupiter, there is very little per cubic kilometer. What we observe as a beautiful comet sweeping across the sky was described by Percival Lowell as "a bagful of nothing." The amount of material in 1000 cubic kilometers of a comet's tail is less than that in 1 cubic centimeter of ordinary air. One form of speculation is about what would happen to the earth if we collided with a comet or its tail. If we hit only the tail, as we may have done in 1861 and 1910, nothing unusual would happen; the sky might be a trifle brighter than usual because we would be looking into the bright stuff of the comet's tail. If the earth met the nucleus of the comet, which probably contains the greater part of all the comet's mass, we might see a very intense meteor shower.

The Light of Comets

If we photograph the light of a comet after dispersing it through a prism, the resulting spectrum differs greatly from that of an asteroid. Down the center of the image, where the bright nucleus of the comet lies, is a continuous band of color from the red to the violet

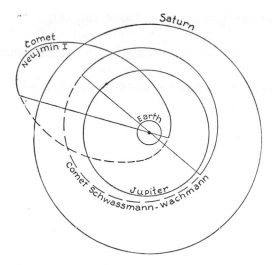

Fig. 33. The orbits of two periodic comets. Comet Schwassmann-Wachmann has a nearly circular orbit which keeps the comet between the orbits of Jupiter and Saturn. Comet Neujmin I is more typical of the known periodic comets. Their orbital inclinations are respectively 9° and 15°; both have periods near 17 yr.

(Plate 15). So far as we can tell, this is principally sunlight reflected from gas and solid material within the nucleus. At various places along this band of color are small images of the comet, each distinctly separate. Some are large and some are small; each tells its own story about the comet.

Before we can properly interpret these separate images, we should photograph the comet through another, more complicated, spectrograph which contains a narrow slit. With a large telescope we concentrate the light of the comet upon this slit, behind which are prisms to disperse the colors and a camera to record them for us. The photograph we obtain, like Plate 16, consists of many little images of the slit, each photographed in a different color. The nucleus again gives us a faint continuous band of color, but the separate images of the comet now appear as narrow lines, or groups of lines close together, whose positions along the spectrum can be measured very accurately.

For an explanation of this result we turn to the physics laboratory and find that only atoms of hot gases give off such patterns of isolated lines, and that gas molecules give off bands of closely grouped lines. By testing various types of gases and carefully noting where their light comes along the spectrum, most of the strong lines in cometary spectra have been identified with gases containing the four elements carbon, hydrogen, oxygen, and nitrogen. The molecules identified, several of which are electrically charged, or ionized, as indicated by a plus sign, are: C_2, CN, CH and CH^+, CO^+, N_2^+, NH, OH and OH^+, CH_2, and NH_2. Most of these molecules are chemically unstable and will combine with other molecules upon contact; they exist in the observed forms only because the gas density in a cometary coma is exceedingly low and molecular collisions are rare. Since these gases are continually being lost from a comet, they must be continually released from some parent material in the comet nucleus. There the parent molecules are suspected to be carbon, C_2; methane, CH_4; ammonia, NH_3; carbon dioxide, CO_2; water, H_2O; and possibly C_2N_2. Through the absorption of sunlight these molecules are broken apart and sometimes ionized to provide the gases observed. Atoms of the four elements may also be present, but are unobservable. Although several of these gases, such as cyanogen (CN), methane, and carbon monoxide, are poisonous, each molecule is separated from its nearest companion by meters or even kilometers. We need fear no chemical poisoning from passing through a comet's tail.

When far from the sun, the principal radiation of a comet comes from CN. As the comet approaches the sun the light of C_2, CH, OH, and NH increases in intensity as the coma brightens. Within the orbit of Mars the radiations of CO^+, OH^+, N_2^+, and CH^+ appear, principally in the budding tail. Observed close to the nucleus are

CH, CH_2, and NH_2. Comets that venture well within the earth's orbit show other progressive spectral changes; some of the radiations fade rapidly, while others brighten. Near the distance of Venus from the sun the yellow light of sodium appears. The great comet 1882 II passed within 500,000 kilometers of the sun, where the surface of the solid nucleus must have been heated to about 3000°C. The spectrum of this comet contained 17 bright lines, of which some were attributed to the atoms of sodium and iron, and some less surely to chromium and nickel. At approximately 20,000,000 kilometers from the sun the bright comet 1947 XII showed, on spectrograms obtained at the McDonald Observatory, radiations from iron and nickel. Since the light of a comet comes from such a mixture of molecules and atoms, each of which changes in brightness with distance from the sun, there is little wonder that prediction of how the brightness of any particular comet will change as it nears the sun is uncertain.

A comet is not a self-luminous body, but shines by sunlight, some of which is reflected by the solid material and some is absorbed and reëmitted by the gas molecules. These molecules are very greedy and can take up large quantities of deep-violet light from the sun and turn it into the colors we can see and photograph. In the process, some of the molecules are broken apart and no longer are detectable. As a comet moves toward perihelion and the intensity of sunlight increases, more and more molecules break apart until at very small solar distances few exist and we see mainly the radiations from the separated atoms evaporated from the solid materials of the nucleus. Theoretical studies of how sunlight disrupts the molecules in comets show that the molecules of CO and N_2 break up less easily than those of C_2, CH, and CN. These latter molecules, when freed within the coma of a comet, are soon torn apart and disappear. The tighter-knit molecules of CO^+ and N_2^+ are ionized and are blown out into the comet's tail, where they are the main visible constituents. As the comet nears the sun, the molecules are broken more rapidly and the apparent size of the coma decreases. This was illustrated by Halley's comet in 1910, which shrank from a diameter of 230,000 kilometers to 40,000 kilometers as it neared perihelion.

The theory of cometary radiation resulting from the studies of Wurm, Swings, and others seems to account for the gases observed, their relative brightness, and their relative positions within a comet's head or tail. Yet, as Bobrovnikoff has pointed out, the theory does not account for the great accelerations that push clouds of gases out into the tails of comets such as Morehouse. Since such large accelerations are observed in only a few comets, they may be associated in some way with the structure of those particular comets rather than with the general mechanism producing cometary luminosity.

Not only does a comet continually lose material into its tail, but several great comets have developed satellitic comets which ran along with them for a few days or weeks before fading from view. One clue to this phenomenon is given by the great comet of 1882. When it passed closest to the sun its nucleus seemed to break into at least four separate parts, like beads on a string. Simultaneously at least one satellitic comet appeared. In 1880 another bright comet had moved in nearly the same orbit and in 1887 a third one moving similarly appeared. We call this concurrence a comet group and wonder if they were not originally one great comet that split when it passed close to the sun at some previous perihelion passage. The disruptive force of the sun at the small perihelion distance of these comets must be terrific and it is surprising that any parts of them could survive a first perihelion passage to return even as fragments at a later time. When comet 1947 XII swung past perihelion only 16,000,000 kilometers from the sun its nucleus split into two parts which varied in their relative brightness. Whether this comet is part of a comet group or just beginning to form a group remains to be seen.

The Comet's Nucleus

No sizable body has ever been observed within the nucleus of a comet. In 1910 Halley's comet passed between the earth and the sun, yet not the slightest sign of the comet could be seen, although a solid body 50 kilometers across would have appeared as a small dot moving across the sun. Comet Pons-Winnecke came very near the earth in 1927 and allowed close scrutiny of its internal structure. Both Baldet and Slipher examined the nucleus under high magnification and concluded that any solid mass in it could not be more than 1 or 2 kilometers across. Indeed, from its brightness Baldet found that the nucleus could not be a solid body larger than 400 meters in diameter.

Observations indicate that no two comets are identical in behavior or, presumably, in internal structure. They brighten near the sun at different rates; some seem to rotate; they seem to differ in the abundance of various chemicals; and some seem to be internally strong while others are weak. As the following chapters on meteors and meteor showers will show, comets spawn myriads of small solid particles. Yet of these, solid chunks weighing as much as a few grams are exceedingly rare. Enormous quantities of gas come out of comets; yet the supply is not unlimited, for some no longer produce tails. Such varied evidence, often seemingly contradictory, has made the construction of a model or "picture" or a comet difficult.

For some time the nucleus was thought to consist of a swarm of independent solid particles, each weighing perhaps a few milligrams and separated by a meter or more. These might surround some larger pieces which could not be many kilometers in diameter. The observed gases were supposed to leak out of the solid particles, but the considerable quantities of gas observed did not seem consistent with slow leakage from solid particles. Furthermore, such an assemblage of individual particles, held together as a swarm only by their weak mutual gravitational attractions, did not satisfy such observations as the continued existence of comet Brooks II after its close approach to Jupiter in 1886.

A Comet Model

Whipple has advanced an interesting comet model that accounts for many of the observed physical and orbital peculiarities and yet provides for differences between comets. He visualizes the nucleus of a comet as a very porous mass of solidified gases, or ices, of H_2O, NH_3, CH_4, and possibly CO_2 and C_2N_2, including occasional solid particles. Perhaps it would look like a very yeasty raisin bread. Such a spongy mass would be a very poor conductor of heat. Although the outer surface would be heated by solar radiation, the inner material would warm up very slowly. From the known properties of the several solidified gases, we see that methane, CH_4, would be the only one to vaporize at solar distances of several astronomical units. Near the distance of Mars, CO_2 and NH_3 would begin to evaporate, and nearer the sun C_2N_2 and H_2O would become gaseous and, through the absorption of sunlight, be broken into less complex molecules. This picture is in general agreement with the spectral changes observed in the coma.

As the outer layers evaporated some of the exposed solid particles would remain attached to the surface and increase the amount of sunlight trapped as heat. Because the mass is spongy, pockets of gas would develop near the surface and would eventually be released to form jets or clouds in the coma. In some comets such pockets of gas might explode, like gas pockets in burning wood, to eject the gas with considerable velocity, thereby possibly producing the high velocities observed in the tails of comet Morehouse and a few other comets.

Since Bobrovnikoff has concluded that the nuclei of many comets rotate, the effects of rotation on the cometary structure must be considered. If the period of rotation is relatively short, some of the gas will not be released when its source is turned directly toward the sun, but later, and hence at a considerable angle to incoming sunlight. This would produce asymmetries in the coma and possibly in the tail.

As material evaporates off the icy nucleus or is ejected by little explosions, the nucleus would be pushed in the other direction. A nonrotating nucleus would then be pushed away from the sun (Fig. 34a), as though the sun's gravitational attraction had been slightly diminished. Whipple suspects that this effect has influenced the motion of comet 1905 III.

For a rotating comet the effects on the orbit should be more pronounced. If the rotation brings the heated side of the nucleus toward the direction of motion (Fig. 34b), the ejected material will push back against the nucleus and slow it down. This results in a decrease in the comet's period and in the orbital eccentricity; thus the orbit becomes smaller and rounder. If, however, the rotation is in the opposite direction, with the gases emitted behind the nucleus (Fig. 34c), the comet speeds up and takes on a larger and more eccentric orbit.

The period of Encke's comet, only 3.3 years, and its orbital eccentricity have long been suspected of decreasing. The rate does not seem to have been constant, but the evidence for such changes has evoked much discussion and the postulation of an interplanetary medium that would slow the comet. If this comet has a retrograde rotation, as in Fig. 34*b* and loses one five-hundredth of its mass at each perihelion passage — a quantity considerably less than Whipple's theory suggests as possible — the observed orbital changes would be accounted for.

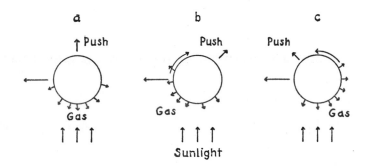

Fig. 34. *Whipple's suggestion of how the ejection of gas from a comet produces a push on the nucleus. The comet is indicated as moving toward the left. In (a) the nucleus does not rotate. In (b) the nucleus rotates clockwise. In (c) the nucleus rotates counterclockwise.*

Comet D'Arrest, period 6.7 years and perihelion distance 1.32 A.U., appears to be pushed forward and to have increasing eccentricity, as though it were rotating in the forward direction, as in Fig. 34*c*. Comet Wolf I also appears to be pushed forward, but it has such a large perihelion distance, 2.4 A.U., that no detectable change in the eccentricity is expected or is found. Dubiago has confirmed Whipple's prediction that comet Brooks II should show secular orbital changes as large as those of comets Encke and D'Arrest, or larger. Comet Brooks II behaves as though it were rotating in the retrograde direction like comet Encke.

Whipple's comet model appears to account for many of the observed physical and orbital properties of comets. It also stimulates the careful and laborious investigation of progressive changes in the motions of periodic comets after allowance for the influences of planetary perturbations. Furthermore, it permits reasonable explanations for the rapid fading of some comets, the splitting of some near the sun, and the formation of meteor streams by the pellets loosened from the shrinking nucleus. Much further investigation and probably some modifications will be required before this model is generally accepted, but it is the first major effort in many decades to organize and interpret the many and varied observations of cometary behavior.

The Origin of Comets

Any attempt to account for the origin of comets must be consistent with both the physical and the orbital properties of these bodies. Until the advent of Whipple's model, in 1949, the orbital information had served as the principal basis for discussion. Yet a number of the discussions involved, by implication, a physical structure not unlike this model. Since the comets cannot tell us how they came into existence, let us see what possibilities we can imagine and how the evidence supports or refutes these ideas.

Either comets were formed in the solar system, or they were formed in interstellar space and through some process were ensnared in the sun's gravitational field. The latter possibility has become more plausible as additional information about the conditions of interstellar matter have accumulated. These vast spaces appear to contain not only highly diffuse gas, but also dust and possibly even larger solid particles. Numerous theoretical investigations have explored mechanisms by which these tenuous clouds might be concentrated to form sizable blocks of ices with imbedded particles. Whether the dark nebulae contain such large bodies is not known, but it does not seem impossible. In the course of several rotations of the galaxy, each requiring, for the sun, about 200,000,000 years, the sun has very likely passed through one or more such clouds. The gravitational attraction of the sun would cause some of these masses to move into the solar system along hyperbolic orbits. Whether or not planetary perturbations and perhaps near collisions between the masses would reduce their high velocity and leave some of them captured is a topic for argument. The physical evidence about comets is not inconsistent with their possible origin in interstellar space, but the dynamics of their possible capture and subsequent motion are debatable.

The definite absence of comets moving in sensibly hyperbolic orbits requires that the comets we see now be permanent members of the solar system. No capture process is operating at present. Had it operated in the relatively recent past, the directions in which parabolic comets move should show some concentrations reminiscent of the original motions, but that is not observed. If the comets were captured, it was some time ago and the vestiges of the process have been erased by perturbations.

Not only has the information about interplanetary material and its progressive condensation supported the idea that comets may have been captured, but it has considerably modified previous ideas about the origin of the solar system. If, as seems likely, stars are constantly being formed from vast accumulations of such interstellar gleanings, they, and the sun too, might be surrounded by a halo of comet-stuff. The question is then whether comets could have existed as members of the solar family throughout the several billion years since the planetary system took form. The available evidence is meager. We discover only comets coming to perihelion within the orbit of Jupiter and know of only a few with perihelion distances greater than 2.5 A.U. It is reasonable to suppose that other comets come to perihelion at distances of 5 to 100 or more astronomical units and remain continually invisible to us. Any comet moving in an orbit of very long period, perhaps several million years, spends at most a brief 50 years at each perihelion passage within the domain of the planets.

Realizing this, Opik some years ago suggested that around the whole solar system there might exist a cometary halo of which only a few parts ever occasionally approached the sun within the planetary orbits. Oort has investigated the effects that the attraction of passing stars would have on such a cometary halo. He, like Opik, concluded that some of the comets would be stolen from the solar system. But Oort found that others would be thrown into elongated orbits that would bring them among the planets. We have already seen how later planetary perturbations would gradually decrease the periods of these comets and cause some of them to remain entirely within the planetary domain.

The likelihood of such processes suggests that the total number of comets attached to the solar system is very large but gradually decreasing. There is, however, a possibility that in the colder regions, beyond the orbit of Jupiter, cometary nuclei are built up from gas atoms and molecules and perhaps solid pellets that freeze together. In this way comets may be rebuilt between perihelion passages.

6

Shooting Stars

Each day billions of tiny particles dash into the earth's atmosphere, appear as brief streaks of light, and vanish. These are meteors, popularly known as shooting stars; a photographic record of one is shown in Plate 17. For many centuries they were thought to be some local phenomenon, like lightning flashes; hence the term meteor, meaning something in the atmosphere. Only a few attempts to study the nature of meteors were made before the end of the eighteenth century. In 1798 two German students, Brandes and Benzenberg, noticed that although they were several kilometers apart they saw the same meteors, but in different parts of the sky. They realized that the meteors could not be nearby phenomena, like lightning flashes; neither could they be at enormous distances, like the moon and the planets. After carefully observing the paths of numerous meteors, they were able to compute the heights and positions of some by the simple process of triangulation, just as a surveyor locates a distant inaccessible mountain (Fig. 35). To visualize the effect, hold a finger at arm's length and notice how its position against the distant background changes when it is viewed alternately with the left and the right eye. From their first observations Brandes and Benzenberg found that meteors flame high above the earth, at altitudes around 80 kilometers. A few rough estimates of how many seconds the meteors were visible showed that they had velocities of

75

at least several kilometers a second and must arise from particles that have come from the parts of space beyond the moon. The term meteor is now often used to refer to either the visible light or the particle.

These results received little attention for over 30 years. On November 12, 1833, however, a great meteor shower once again at-

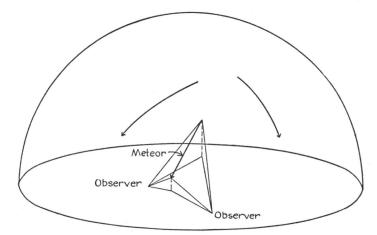

Fig. 35. The path of a meteor through the atmosphere and the apparent paths as seen by two widely separated observers.

tracted attention to these celestial fireworks. Several persons independently noticed that the paths of the meteors seemed to spread out from a point in the constellation Leo, much as the ribs of an umbrella spread out from the tip. To interpret this effect we need only notice how the parallel sides of a long room seem to converge in the distance. If we trace the meteor paths backward they too converge in the distance, at a point called their radiant. This effect of perspective can mean only one thing: the meteors of the shower moved in parallel orbits before they hit the earth and must constitute a great stream of bodies moving around the sun. This discovery established that meteors are of astronomical significance and worthy of extensive study.

Observing Meteors

During the past century many other showers have been noticed. Table 13 summarizes some of the characteristics of the most conspicuous annual showers, identified by the constellations in which their radiants lie. But not all meteors can be identified with recognized showers; most are sporadic and provide a background against which the shower meteors appear.

Table 13. Characteristics of some annual meteor showers.

Shower	Date of maximum	Radiant		Velocity (km/sec)
		R.A. (deg)	Dec. (deg)	
Quadrantid	January 3	231	51	40.9
Lyrid	April 21	280	37	48.6
Eta Aquarid	May 4	336	− 1	60
Delta Aquarid	July 29	340	−17	40.3
Perseid	August 12	45	57	60.5
Orionid	October 22	96	15	66.5
Taurid, North	November 1	51	14	31–25
South	November 16	60	23	32–26
Leonid	November 17	152	22	72
Geminid	December 12	113	32	35.4

Unfortunately a meteor gives no warning of its impending dash into the atmosphere. Suddenly it flames across the sky and abruptly disappears. What it is and whence it came must be determined from the observations secured in those few seconds that cannot be anticipated. When we go meteor observing we must take potluck. Professional astronomers have no better fortune than amateurs, and the study of meteors is one field of astronomy in which amateurs, working according to prearranged schedules and programs, aid the professional astronomers.

Meteors differ greatly in brightness. Some are so brilliant they floodlight several states as they blaze to oblivion; a few are seen even in daylight. These brightest meteors are generally termed fireballs, but how bright they must be to warrant this special designation is a matter of choice. One astronomer adopted a very practical definition: "A fireball is a meteor sufficiently bright to make people report it." The great majority of meteors, the ordinary shooting stars, are, however, relatively faint and can be seen only at night against a moonless sky. Many additional meteors are so faint they can be seen only through binoculars or wide-angle telescopes.

Only a few thousand fireballs appear over the earth each day and, no matter how diligent the observer, he could not possibly be always alert on the chance that he might see one. Before routine photographic trapping was introduced, astronomers had to rely chiefly upon the descriptions of unskilled observers who were amazed by the awe-inspiring spectacle of a great fireball bursting into view. They eloquently described what they saw, but often forgot that the astronomer needs accurate facts on directions, angular elevations, and durations. The astronomer's task is further complicated by the fact that our urban population often has only the haziest concepts of direction even in familiar surroundings. An interesting psychological effect frequently reported is the feeling that the meteor fell to the earth "next door," "in the next block," or "in that pile of leaves," even though it was several hundred kilometers away. By sifting and weighting numerous reports of this type astronomers can sometimes derive a bright meteor's path through the atmosphere.

Even an experienced observer is badly handicapped in studying ordinary meteors, for he never knows when or where the next one will appear. Suddenly he must locate its path among the stars and estimate its duration and brightness with accuracy. A further complication comes through the observer's predilection to draw the trails longer or shorter than they really were or to displace them to the right or left from their actual positions. Even so, the average heights at which meteors appear and disappear are well known from careful visual observations. For the ordinary meteors the heights of appearance are consistently near 100 kilometers, irrespective of their later maximum brightness (Fig. 36). The bright ones, however, penetrate deepest into the atmosphere. Great fireballs which rival the full moon in brightness are visible to even lower levels, many to nearly 40 kilometers, while those from which meteorites fall often blaze to within 20 kilometers of the ground. Meteors belonging to the strong streams, some of which meet the earth's atmosphere head-on, seem to appear near 115 kilometers, a bit higher than the average meteor of the same brightness.

Occasionally the reports about a fireball indicate that it appeared as high as 200 kilometers above the earth. Such values are rare among the records of experienced observers and these extreme heights are now generally held under suspicion. Wylie made experiments that required inexperienced observers to respond to artificial fireballs and found that the observers extended the meteor's path backward, thereby exaggerating the height at which it appeared. Furthermore, such great heights of appearance seem to be inconsistent with our growing knowledge of the atmosphere's structure and the processes causing meteoric luminosity.

Velocities and Orbits

As we found for comets, the orbital velocities of meteors determine whether they are permanent members of the solar system or

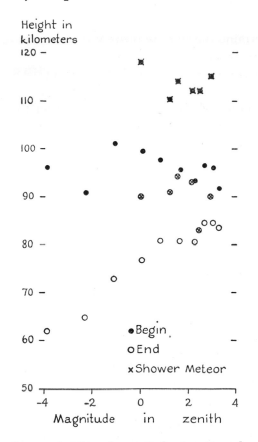

Fig. 36. *Relation between height and magnitude of meteors observed visually. According to the Arizona Meteor Expedition, the heights at which meteors appear change little with their magnitude, but bright meteors penetrate much lower than do faint ones. Shower meteors seem to begin and end somewhat higher than do nonshower meteors.*

79

have wandered in from the depths of space. Our problem of deciding on which side of the parabolic velocity the sporadic meteors come is complicated by the fact that nearly all the periodic orbits in which they are likely to move have velocities very near the parabolic limit. For example, a particle moving with a period of 27 years, in an orbit having a semimajor axis of 9 A.U., has, at the earth's distance from the sun, a velocity of 41.0 kilometers per second. This differs from the critical value, 42.1 kilometers per second, by less than 3 percent. If we are to derive significant orbits, we must have accurate velocities. Many scientists have carefully tried to find velocities from direct visual observations but they eventually concluded that they could not determine the path lengths and durations of meteors with the required accuracy.

Because the earth moves around the sun at 29.8 kilometers per second, we run into some meteors and run away from others. As a result, the velocities of the meteors with respect to the earth differ considerably from their velocities with respect to the sun. In Fig. 37

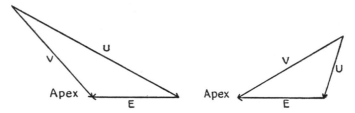

Fig. 37. *Combination of velocities. The earth's velocity* E *combines with the meteor's real velocity* V *to make it enter our atmosphere with the speed and direction represented by* U.

we let the arrow *E* represent the earth's orbital velocity of 30 kilometers per second and direction of motion around the sun. The place in the sky toward which this arrow points is called the apex of the earth's motion. The meteor's speed and direction are indicated by *V*. If the earth meets the meteor head-on, it rushes into the atmosphere at 72 kilometers per second. If, however, the earth runs away from the meteor, it overtakes us at only 12 kilometers per second. When the meteor moves across the earth's orbit, *V* and *E* combine to form the line *U*, which indicates the speed and direction of the meteor's dash into the atmosphere. The earth's motion not only alters a meteor's apparent speed, but also shifts the observed radiant toward the apex of the earth's motion, that is, the point toward which the earth is moving. As the earth moves around the sun, the observed velocity of a continuing shower will change and the radiant may shift by as much as 1 degree per day.

The earth pulls on the meteors and speeds them up to a velocity W somewhat larger than U. The amount of this effect is given by $W^2 = U^2 + 125$, when W and U are in kilometers per second. As an interesting result of this relation we notice that even if the meteor had no original motion with respect to the earth, that is, even if $U = 0$, the earth's attraction would make it strike the atmosphere at 11 kilometers per second.

For many years unsuccessful attempts were made to devise techniques by which the average velocity of meteors with respect to the sun could be determined from quantities accurately and easily observed. As early as 1866 Schiaparelli pointed out that in the morning hours we are on the forward side of the earth, as shown in Fig. 38,

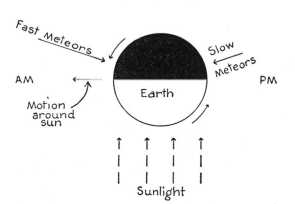

Fig. 38. *Diurnal effects upon meteors. In the evening the observer is on the back of the moving earth and observes only meteors that overtake us. In the morning he is on the forward side and meets the meteors head-on.*

and see meteors that we encounter, at high speed. In the evening we are on the back side of the earth and see only meteors that overtake us, at low speed. The change in frequency between dusk and dawn, observed as a factor of three to four, might be used to indicate the average speeds of the meteors. Unfortunately the brightness of a meteor, by which we see it, is so dependent upon the speed and direction of motion that the average speed could not be derived satisfactorily from the observations of frequency.

Numerous observers, especially in England, labored arduously to derive reliable velocities from observations of individual meteors. In addition, the Arizona Meteor Expedition, sponsored by Harvard and Cornell Universities, attempted similar studies. Despite ingenious observing techniques and careful analysis, the inherent uncertainties were too great to provide a definite answer about what fraction, if any, of the meteors had not been permanent members of the solar system. The problem has, however, been solved. The more accurate photographic and radio observations, to be discussed later, indicate that essentially all meteors have been permanent members of the solar system. Many move in orbits of quite short period.

Meteor Photography

The possibilities of recording meteors photographically have long been recognized. The earliest meteor photograph, secured in Prague on November 27, 1885, recorded a meteor belonging to the great Andromede shower of that year. Since then many meteors have left their marks on photographs exposed at various observatories. For more than 60 years the Harvard Observatory has systematically photographed the sky and accumulated nearly half a million plates, which show the trails of more than a thousand bright meteors. The majority of these were recorded accidentally in the course of other routine photographic work, as in Plate 18, although a few were trapped by cameras operated especially for meteors on nights when showers were expected. If you anticipate photographing meteors, be well supplied with patience. On average nights a typical F/4.5 camera having a field of 60° traps one meteor in about 100 exposure hours. When a strong shower develops, such as the Perseid shower in mid-August, the rate may increase to one meteor in 5 exposure hours. These photographed meteors will be brighter than magnitude zero, which is about the faintest that can be recorded with such a camera and the most sensitive film.

Our most precise values of the velocities of meteors come through the use of impersonal automatic photographic records. In 1893 Elkin of Yale began a systematic program for photographing meteors from two stations. By rotating a shutter, made from a bicycle wheel, at a known rate in front of the camera lenses, he broke each meteor trail into segments which revealed the meteor's velocity. Unfortunately, the distance between his two stations was insufficient to yield results of satisfactory accuracy. Since then other people have photographed meteors from two stations, but no continuing efforts to determine velocities were begun until 1936.

One of the Harvard Observatory's short-focus cameras in Cambridge and another at the Agassiz Station, 38 kilometers away, operated from 1936 to 1948 upon schedules so synchronized that they were both directed toward an area 80 kilometers above the earth. Any bright meteor passing through this area recorded itself on the two photographs. Each camera lens was occulted by a thin blade, like a windmill, similar to that in Plate 19, which segmented the photographed trails 20 times each second. This provided a means for accurately computing the velocities (Fig. 39) and orbits. Similar photographic equipment and programs have also been established in the U.S.S.R. and in Japan.

In 1948, under the supervision of Whipple, the Harvard cameras were moved to new sites in New Mexico where clear skies are more frequent. In 1952 these cameras were replaced by very fast Baker-Super-Schmidt cameras, as shown in Plate 20, which operate at F/0.67. Each covers an area of the sky 55° across. The rotating shutter makes 60 brief exposures each second, but cuts off starlight and fogging skylight for a considerable percent of the exposure time. These cameras are able to record most of the meteors observed visually and thereby yield velocities for meteors much fainter than previously photographed. With them the average exposure time per meteor photographed has decreased to only 18 minutes; this supplies an overwhelming volume of records for analysis. A typical pair of meteors photographed with these cameras is shown in Plate 21. For the study of latitude effects in atmospheric structure, similar cameras have also been put into operation in Canada. From these various photographic programs the total number of doubly photographed meteors has approached 4000.

From the systematic Harvard meteor patrol, orbits have been

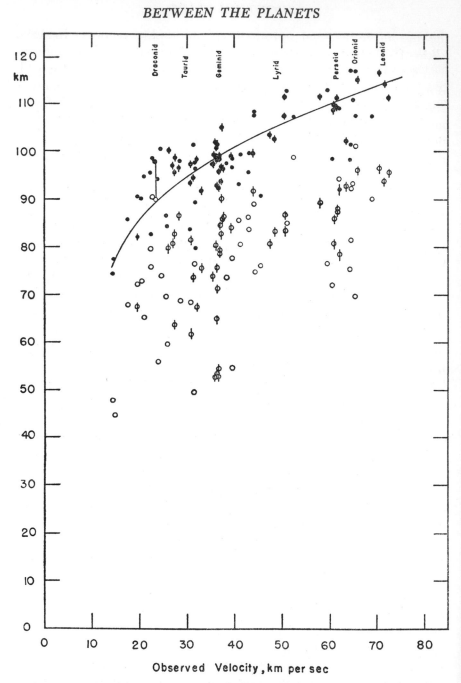

Fig. 39. Relation between height and velocity of 85 photographed meteors analyzed by Whipple and Jacchia. The symbols used are: solid circle, beginning height; open circle, ending height; vertical bar, shower meteor. The mean heights of appearance and disappearance of 206 Draconid meteors, studied by Jacchia, Kopal and Millman, are indicated by the vertical line.

derived for 51 sporadic meteors as well as for many shower meteors. Of the 51 sporadics, after allowance for the small observational uncertainties, not one had an orbit that was certainly hyperbolic. Of the 17 with retrograde orbits, only one had a period less than 22 years and an aphelion distance less than 8 A.U.

The frequencies of orbital inclinations derived for 21 meteor streams and 51 nonstream, or sporadic, meteors are shown in Table 14. For the sporadic meteors Whipple has derived the likelihood of

Table 14. *Distribution of orbital inclinations of meteor streams and sporadic meteors; comparison of cosmic frequency of sporadic meteors with cometary frequencies.*

Range in i (deg)	Number of showers	Number of sporadic meteors	Cosmic frequency of sporadic meteors (percent)	Percentage of comets with periods less than	
				200 yr	8.6 yr
0– 10	7	13	22	32	38
10– 20	2	12	39	36	46
20– 30	3	3	10	8	9
30– 60	3	5	14	13	6
60– 90	2	2	3	4	0
90–120	1	3	5	4	1
120–150	1	9	6	1	0
150–180	2	4	1	2	0
Total	21	51	100	100	100

collision with the earth and corrected the observed frequencies to their cosmic frequencies. These show that most of the sporadic meteors have orbits similar to those of comets with periods less than 200 years. Like the comets, both stream and sporadic meteors have a high concentration of orbits with inclinations less than 35°, and the orbital inclinations tend to increase with period. Whipple doubts that more than 10 to 15 percent of the photographed sporadic meteors can be of asteroidal origin; most seem to arise from cometary debris.

As meteors plunge into the lower and denser regions of the atmosphere their motions are retarded. From interrupted trails photographed from two observing stations the small changes in velocity can often be determined. Near the point of appearance at heights around 100 kilometers the deceleration is small, but it increases rapidly as the meteor descends. In combination with a theory of meteor luminescence, these decelerations yield information on the density of the upper atmosphere and its seasonal variations. In conjunction with similar data from high-altitude rockets, meteor observations are refining our picture of the atmosphere, as sketched in Fig. 40.

From observations of the decelerations, general meteor theory, and the variations of atmospheric pressure with altitude, approximate preatmospheric masses for the meteors can be found. Jacchia found the masses of 50 meteors to range from a fraction of a gram up to about a kilogram for one slow but very bright sporadic meteor. In general, the masses of these photographed meteors were of the order of a few grams.

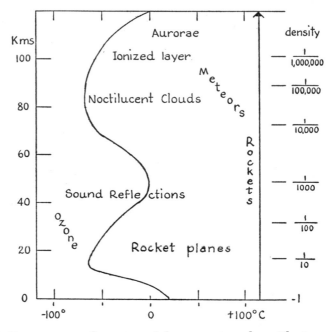

Fig. 40. *Temperature and structure of the upper atmosphere. The temperatures are on the centigrade scale, which has 0° for freezing water and 100° for boiling water. The rapid drop in density is evident from the scale at the right.*

Although radar and radio observations of meteors are discussed in Chapter 8, for completeness some of the velocity results must be anticipated here. Several extensive sets of records clearly indicate that if any meteors have hyperbolic velocities, they are less than 1 percent of the total. This result includes visual meteors and those in the telescopic range down to magnitudes estimated as the ninth. Furthermore, the distribution of velocities (Fig. 47) shows two peaks of frequency. A large number of meteors have observed velocities between 30 and 45 kilometers per second. A second maximum occurs between 55 and 65 kilometers per second. Very few velocities are close to the parabolic limit of 72 kilometers per second.

Spectra and Composition of Meteors

When a glass prism is placed in front of a camera, the light of a meteor can be dispersed into its component colors, as a spectrum, and photographed. Up to 1930 only eight meteor spectra had been photographed, all by accident. While at the Harvard Observatory in 1931 Millman began a routine program of spectrum photography. Within a few years several groups of amateurs joined in the work and by 1952, mainly through the efforts of observers in Canada, the Soviet Union, and the United States, the number of photographed spectra exceeded 120. The meteors producing these spectra were assigned visual magnitudes between 0 and -9.

In Plate 22 are shown two typical meteor spectra, which consist of isolated bright lines. As only gases give such bright-line spectra, the light we see arises in an envelope of hot gas. Millman has grouped these spectra into two classes: type Y, containing two strong lines, known as H and K, due to ionized calcium, and type Z, from which these lines were absent.

Although some of the spectra are more detailed than others, all are of some value. Of 104 spectra Millman identified 75 with five strong showers. All spectra of these shower meteors are similar but differ in excitation, which is associated with the velocity, as shown by Plate 22. Of 15 nonshower spectra of good quality, eight show no calcium ions (type Z), while seven do show calcium ions (type Y). Whether there is a fundamental difference between the spectra of shower and nonshower meteors remains to be seen, for some now listed as nonshower may later be identified with weak showers. The importance of care in matching spectral type and orbital characteristics is emphasized by Table 15, in which the slower shower meteors show neutral calcium, but do not show calcium ions.

87

The spectral differences of nonshower meteors may be only a velocity effect.

Inasmuch as chemical analyses have been made of many large meteorites, which were not completely consumed during their dash

Table 15. *Spectral characteristics of shower meteors.*

Shower	Number of spectra	Velocity (km/sec)	Description
Draconid	26	23	Low excitation, no ions, strong sodium, weak neutral calcium
Geminid	10	35	Weak calcium ions
Perseid	25	60	Strong ions of Ca, Mg, Si
Orionid	1	66	Like Perseid
Leonid	13	72	Like Perseid

through the atmosphere, we may compare meteor spectra (Table 16) to those expected from meteorites. The numerous metallic meteorites contain little or no calcium, whose radiations are prominent in many meteor spectra. But calcium is also absent from some

Table 16. *Chemical elements found in 44 meteor spectra.*

Element	Number of spectra
Iron	37
Calcium ion	33
Calcium	17
Manganese	9
Magnesium	7
Chromium	3
Magnesium ion	2
Silicon ion	2
Silicon	2
Nickel	2
Aluminum	2
Sodium	1

stony meteorites and is rarely abundant in the others (Table 17). Prior observed, however, that when calcium is absent magnesium is fairly abundant. The appearance of radiations from either calcium or magnesium, rather than just the appearance or absence of calcium alone, may be a more satisfactory criterion for the classification of meteor spectra. The frequent appearance of calcium in meteor spectra, implying origin from stony particles, and the paucity of what appear to be small metallic particles seems to be significant.

A meteor results when a little particle moving with a speed of many kilometers per second smashes into the atoms and molecules of our protecting atmosphere. These atmospheric atoms collide with the solid particle so violently that they chip atoms from its surface and send them flying away with high energy to form a cloud of gas with a temperature of several thousand degrees. This atomic pecking continues until the small solid particle is completely consumed. Occasionally the particles, spinning around like pinwheels, make flares along their paths. Others split into several parts, while some end their existence in a final bright burst, as in Plate 18.

Average meteors never reach the ground and cannot be weighed. But their sizes can be found from studies of how large the particles

Table 17. *Abundance of magnesium, calcium, sodium, and aluminum in 59 meteorites.*

Element	Abundance (percent)		
	Maximum	Minimum	Mean
Magnesium	21.6	4.3	14.3
Calcium	17.5	0.0	1.3
Sodium	2.9	0.0	0.6
Aluminum	7.2	0.1	1.5

must be to produce the light we see, for their brightness depends chiefly upon their speed and size. The theory indicates that the brightness of ordinary meteors changes proportionally to the mass — a large particle makes a bright meteor. The brightness also changes very rapidly with velocity, the fastest moving particles making the brightest meteors. A second-magnitude meteor of the Perseid shower, with a velocity of 60 kilometers per second, has a mass of a few milligrams — about that of a pinhead. At the low velocity of the Draconid shower, 23 kilometers per second, this same particle would produce a meteor of only the fifth magnitude, barely visible on a clear moonless night.

The theory of how a fast-moving particle forms a visible meteor now permits densities to be derived for the particles. Surprisingly, many of the photographed meteors arise from particles having densities less than one. They would float on water. Such particles also seem to be quite fragile and crumble readily under small pressures. This result strongly suggests that many of the meteors arise from icy particles similar to those that might be expected from Whipple's ice model of comets.

Meteor Trains

Nearly all meteors of zero magnitude or brighter leave in their wake a glowing streak, or train, like that shown in Plate 23. For common meteors these trains last little more than a second, but for very bright meteors they last from several minutes to a half hour or more. Immediately after the meteor passes, its train begins to expand and often forms within 2 or 3 seconds a hollow cylinder a kilometer across and several kilometers long. In 1949 Millman photographed the spectrum of a Perseid train that showed bright lines identified with iron, magnesium, calcium, and possibly sodium. No radiations from ions were found.

The duration of the train is associated not only with the brightness of the meteor but also with its velocity; the faster, hotter meteors like the Leonids have the most conspicuous trains. Plavec found that trains were observed for about half of the Perseids, but for only 5 percent of the slower Geminids. Another peculiarity of the trains is their occurrence above the height of 82 kilometers where the temperature of the atmosphere reaches a minimum ($-70°C$).

Bright meteors frequently penetrate well below this level, but leave trains of longest duration at heights near 90 kilometers. Meteor trains are probably associated with many other phenomena occurring near this cold zone: meteors flare up most commonly at this level; radio waves are reflected from the heavily ionized Kennelly-Heaviside layer near this height; noctilucent clouds, rarely seen in America, occur there; and auroral streamers and arcs extend upward from this region. All of these phenomena, some of which are electrical, may be related to one another and to the formations and preservation of self-luminous meteor trains.

Another type of meteor train consists of smoke and dust illuminated by sunlight. These occur only in the wake of very bright meteors — those likely to drop meteorites — which penetrate to the lower regions of the atmosphere. Since such bright fireballs are rare, and only a few of them leave great quantities of dust and debris along their paths, dust trains are among the rarest of meteoric phenomena. The most conspicuous sunlit trains occur at twilight when they, being high in the atmosphere, are illuminated by the sun, while the observers below are in darkness. One such train over eastern Canada is shown in Plate 24; the original photograph was taken by a quick-minded amateur using an inexpensive camera. The train was visible for an hour and a half, but this seems to be the only photograph made of it. When compared with visual observations from distant places this picture showed that the train was 600 kilometers from the observer, at heights of from 48 to 80 kilometers over the southern tip of Hudson Bay.

One interesting feature of all meteor trains is their rapid deformation, turning from straight lines into twisted forms within a few minutes after their appearance. Furthermore, the trains usually drift horizontally and sometimes move vertically. Such writhing and drifting demonstrate the existence of winds in the high upper atmosphere, winds with hurricane velocities, up to 200 kilometers per hour.

Counting Meteors

On a clear moonless night a single observer will see about 10 meteors per hour; the actual number depends upon the time of night, the season of the year, and the blackness of the sky. Although this rate may seem small to the observer, it indicates a tremendous number of similar meteors appearing over the whole earth per day. The observer's field of view is about 60° in diameter, which, at an altitude of 80 kilometers, covers an area of 5000 square kilometers. Since the total area of the atmosphere is approximately 500,000,000 square kilometers, we see one meteor in each hundred thousand; our 10 meteors per hour means a total of 24,000,000 over the whole earth each day.

Twenty-four million meteors visible each day is a sizable catch for a tiny body like the earth. Yet the real total far exceeds this, for many faint meteors are not noticed by the observers, while other fainter ones can be seen only through telescopes. If the observer carefully records how many meteors of each magnitude he sees, he will find the greatest numbers at the third and fourth magnitudes.

According to his records the total number of each magnitude each day over the earth would be very near those in the second column of Table 18. But this typical observer and every other observer fails to notice many faint meteors at the edge of his field of view. Opik compared the records of four nearby but independent observers and found that each recorded nine-tenths of the meteors of the third magnitude, one-half of those of the fourth magnitude, and one-twelfth of those of the fifth magnitude. When the observed numbers are corrected for these omissions, the total daily numbers become those in the third column of the table. We find there that the meteors

Table 18. *The number and mass of meteors striking the earth each day.*

Visual magnitude	Observed number	Actual number	Mass (mg)	Total mass (kg)
−3	28,000	28,000	4,000	110
−2	71,000	71,000	1,600	110
−1	180,000	180,000	630	110
0	450,000	450,000	250	110
1	1,100,000	1,100,000	100	110
2	2,800,000	2,800,000	40	110
3	6,400,000	7,100,000	16	110
4	9,000,000	18,000,000	6.3	110
5	3,600,000	45,000,000	2.5	110
6		110,000,000	1.0	110
7		280,000,000	0.40	110
8		710,000,000	0.16	110
9		1,800,000,000	0.063	110
10		4,500,000,000	0.025	110

of the fifth magnitude and brighter total 75,000,000 per day. Customarily in these studies meteor magnitudes are corrected to the value they would have had if observed directly overhead, that is, in the zenith.

Through binoculars and low-power telescopes additional faint meteors can be seen. Observations through binoculars indicate that to the eighth magnitude in the zenith the total daily meteor catch over the whole earth must be about 500,000,000. With a low-power telescope the total meteor frequency to the tenth magnitude in the zenith has been found to be near one hundred times that to the fifth magnitude, or a total of several billion per day. The number of meteors seems to increase approximately 2.5 times with each fainter magnitude, or 100 times for five magnitude steps. With this rate of increase Table 18 may be extended to the tenth magnitude to indicate a total of 8,000,000,000 observable meteors entering the earth's atmosphere daily.

Additional smaller particles probably encounter the earth but escape observation as meteors. In the discussion of comet tails we saw that particles smaller than 1 micron in diameter would be blow out of the solar system. But there are many bits of dust slightly larger. These may sift through the atmosphere as micrometeorites without encountering enough continued resistance to be vaporized. Evidence for the reality of such micrometeorites comes from a number of observers who have collected from roofs and from rain water fine particles a few microns across. Among the particles are spherical bodies and others of irregular angular shape. Some of the particles are attracted by a magnet, as though they were rich in iron. Spectrographic analysis of such particles shows them to contain iron, silicon, and magnesium. There is a growing belief that these are actually micrometeorites, but conclusive tests of their extraterrestrial origin are elusive.

Further evidence in support of such an infall of micrometeorites comes from long cores taken from sediments at the bottom of the oceans. These cores react to chemical tests for nickel and show bands of varied nickel concentration. High-altitude rockets also appear to encounter many small particles in the upper regions of our atmosphere. Some observers also report an increase in the fall of dust particles a few days after strong meteor showers. The average rate of collection seems to exceed a million tons a year for the whole earth. This amount exceeds by a thousandfold the weight of material caught by the earth as meteorites or luminous meteors.

The total fall of meteoric material, from the fireballs that drop meteorites to the faintest telescopic meteors, can be estimated when we know the masses of the individual meteors at each magnitude. Knowing the mass of a second-magnitude meteor and assuming the average velocity as 55 kilometers per second, we find the average mass of a typical meteor of magnitude zero to be 250 milligrams — the weight of a few drops of water. Since the brightness of a meteor changes with its mass, a fifth-magnitude meteor, giving only 1 percent as much light as one of magnitude zero, arises from a particle of 2.5 milligrams. When we put such values into Table 18, the total mass for each magnitude interval comes out constant.

To obtain the total mass we need not add up the contributions of a very great number of magnitudes. The very largest bodies crash through the atmosphere and fall to the earth as meteorites. In Chapter 9 we shall add up their mass and find it to be about half a ton per day, which represents all the meteors brighter than magnitude −10. With the use of Table 18 we can add up the masses of all meteors over a range of some twenty magnitudes, −10 to +10, and find a total of a few tons per day. The fine dust particles and micrometeorites seem much more abundant, with a daily rate of infall of between 1000 and perhaps 10,000 tons per day. These amounts and the type of bodies from which they come are summarized in Table 19. In Chapter 11 we shall find that the zodiacal light provides additional evidence for the great amount of small material that is the principal contributor to the earth's gain in mass.

Table 19. Daily rate of meteoritic infall.

Type	Mass accumulated daily (tons)
Crater-producing and other meteorites	< 1
Fireballs Visual meteors Faint radio meteors Telescopic meteors	1–10
Very faint telescopic meteors Micrometeorites Interplanetary dust	1,000–10,000

These estimates of the amount of material swept up each day by the earth are necessarily crude. Yet it seems that each day the earth grows by over a thousand tons of material. While this is a sizable amount, the earth is so large that each year this material adds about 1 kilogram to each square kilometer of area, or 5 to 10 pounds per square mile.

☆

☆ **7** ☆

Meteor Showers

A magnificent display of shooting stars startled the inhabitants of the Americas on November 12, 1833. Beginning before midnight, the meteors increased in frequency until at dawn they were as thick as snow flakes. A single observer often saw twenty appear within a second, spreading out from the constellation Leo, as depicted in Plate 25. Many superstitious people thought this marked the end of the world and, as bells tolled, they prepared for the future. Next day all was serene, but a new branch of astronomy, the study of meteors, had been founded.

This great display and the others that occur from time to time present some of the most interesting but tantalizing information we have about the occupants of interplanetary space. We know nothing of these flying gravel banks until we collide with them and have a great meteor shower. Even afterward we cannot accurately trace their paths through space to predict when we may encounter them again, for when between the planets they are invisible to us. The earth is playing a game of cosmic blindman's buff with them; only if by chance we meet one of these swarms of particles does a brilliant meteor shower result, otherwise we go swinging around the sun, completely ignorant of where or how the meteor swarms are moving.

After 1833 the Leonids were less numerous each year, until soon the shower was inconspicuous. According to diaries, unusual numbers of meteors had also appeared in November for a few years preceding 1833; it appears that the earth cut through the great swarm of bodies several years in a row, then for many years met only a few stragglers. On November 11, 1799 Humboldt had observed a similar shower over South America. This suggested that the display reappeared in November at intervals of 33 or 34 years (Fig. 41). With these clues H. A. Newton traced the shower back through history as far as A.D. 902, when it occurred on October 20; planetary perturbations gradually altered the orbit and changed the date of the shower. Between 902 and 1833 some record of unusual numbers of meteors in late October or early November has been found at intervals of 33 years.

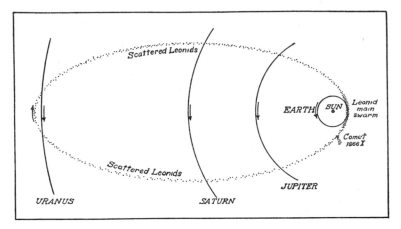

Fig. 41. The orbit of the Leonid meteors. This great swarm requires 33 yr to move around its path. The meteors are so far extended along the orbit that the earth cuts through the dense part of the swarm several years in a row.

According to this periodicity, another shower should have come in 1866. Several years earlier it began to build up and appeared on schedule with an intensity equal to the shower of 1833. Consequently 33 years later astronomers and laymen alike were anticipating the greatest display of celestial fireworks of their lives. Alas! they were disappointed. Between 1866 and 1899 the meteors passed near both Saturn and Jupiter; these planets pulled the particles aside so that the earth passed through only the fringes of the swarm. As 1932 approached and the possibility of another shower was apparent, many people hoped that some perturbation had swung the particles into their previous orbit. As in 1899, the meteors came at the rate of one a minute, but compared to the earlier displays this was disappointing. It is not likely that we shall again witness great displays from this stream. The earth is a mere speck in space, which the meteors can easily pass without striking. The chances that as the perturbations change the meteors' orbit they will again collide with the earth are about equal to the chance that a searchlight capriciously playing over a crowd will again shine on a particular person.

The radiant point of the Leonid meteor shower is within 6° of the direction toward which the earth is moving at that time in its path around the sun. Since this region of the sky does not rise until near midnight, the meteors from that direction do not appear until the morning hours. The Leonids meet the earth head-on, entering the atmosphere at the high speed of 72 kilometers per second. An unusually large number of them leave streaks or enduring trains in their paths.

In the century since 1833 many other meteor showers have been recognized. Some appear regularly each year, others, like the Leonids, at longer intervals, while some have appeared only once or twice. Almost immediately after the Leonid shower of 1833 the unusual number of meteors in early August was recognized as a shower radiating from the constellation Perseus. Each year with perfect regularity meteors stream from Perseus for several weeks, reaching a maximum frequency on August 12. During more than a century the annual number of Perseids has changed so little that we are hard put to detect their period of motion around the sun. Instead of an elongated cluster like the Leonids, the Perseids constitute a great stream of meteors uniformly spaced along their orbit. From the position of their radiant point we can derive an approximate orbit, which has one especially interesting feature: it is tilted almost at right angles to the plane of the earth's motion. Only by accident do the Perseids pass through the orbit of the earth, which is too small to perturb them appreciably. At no time do they pass near a large planet. We may conclude, therefore, that the Perseids have been moving in much the same path for thousands of years, during which time they have gradually become uniformly spread around their entire orbit.

Cometary Association of Meteor Showers

In 1862 a comet faintly visible without a telescope moved across the northern sky. As a comet it was nothing unusual, but in 1866 Schiaparelli noticed that its orbit was almost identical with that of the Perseids. This discovery strongly hinted that the meteor showers and the comets were generically related. Later when the orbit of the faint comet 1866 I was published, Peters, Schiaparelli, and von Oppolzer simultaneously saw that it had the same path as the Leonids. This second identification set off a real hunt for other pairs of comets and meteor showers moving in identical orbits. Soon the Lyrid meteors, another reliable shower appearing late in April, were identified with comet 1861 I. Other periodic comets that pass near the earth's orbit were placed on the list of suspects and each newly recognized shower was compared with them for possible identification. The number of coincident orbits has increased until now those listed in Table 20 are considered as very probably associated. We therefore have good reasons for concluding that each meteor stream originated from a comet.

Halley's comet, in addition to being one of the most conspicuous comets, may provide us with not one, but two, meteor showers. In May, meteors radiate from Aquarius near the star Eta while in October another shower radiates from the head of Orion. Both showers, according to Olivier, move in nearly the same orbit as Halley's comet — we seem to run into the meteors first as they are approaching and then again as they are leaving perihelion. Such a double shower can result only if the original orbit is turned in a particular manner such that the meteors are at the earth's distance from the sun each time they cross the earth's orbital plane; the orbit of Halley's comet is turned in this way. Since in October, when the Orionid meteors appear, the earth is 15,000,000 kilometers from the comet's orbit, the meteors must be very widely scattered. The Eta Aquarids and the Orionids are almost equally abundant each year, when they appear during a period of more than a week. This is what we would expect if the earth did cut through the outer fringes of a very widely scattered stream. Halley's comet undergoes rather periodic perturbations which would aid in scattering along its orbit any particles that strayed a bit ahead or behind.

The Andromedes, or Bielids

Short-period comets as well as those like Halley's and 1866 I also provide meteor showers. As early as 1832, astronomers noted that the orbit of Biela's comet passed within a few thousand kilometers of the earth's path (Fig. 25), and that the earth and the comet might collide. When the orbit of a comet is known, we can compute the date and the radiant point at which associated meteors should appear. In 1798, Brandes observed on the proper date a strong meteor shower, which probably came from this comet. During the next decades a few other meteors moving in the comet's orbit appeared from Andromeda, but nothing spectacular happened until 1872, 20

Table 20. Orbits of some meteor showers and associated comets.

Shower and Comet	ω (deg)	Ω (deg)	i (deg)	e	a (A.U.)	q (A.U.)	P (yr)	U * (km/sec)
Perseids	155	138	116	0.96	22.6	0.96	108	60.5 P
Comet 1862 III	153	138	114	.96	24.7	.96	122	
Leonids	179	233	163	.91	10.3	.99	33	72.0 P
Comet 1866 I	171	231	163	.91	10.3	.98	33	
Lyrids	213	30	80	1.0†		.90		48.6 P
Comet 1861 I	213	30	80	0.98	56.	.92	415	
Andromedes	222	246	13	.75		.86		16.
Biela's Comet, 1852 III	223	246	13	.70	3.52	.86	6.6	
Eta Aquarids	100	45	162	.97		.60		60. R
Halley's Comet	112	57	162	.97	17.9	.59	76	
Orionids	143	28	161	1.0†		.52		66.5 P
Draconids	175	196	31	0.71	3.52	1.00	6.6	23.3
Comet Giacobini-Zinner, 1946 V	172	196	31	.72	3.64	1.00	6.96	
Taurids	109	47	5	.82	2.22	0.39	3.3	30.6 P
Encke's Comet	185	335	13	.85	2.22	.33	3.3	
Umids	206	271	54	.84		.94		33.4
Comet Tuttle I	207	270	55	.82	5.73	1.02	13.7	
Geminids ‡	324	261	24	.90	1.37	0.14	1.6	36.4 P
Delta Aquarids ‡	154	305	30	.97	2.35	.06	3.6	43.0 P
Quadrantids ‡	170	282	72	.72	3.66	1.00	7.0	44.1 P

* P, photographic, R, radio.
† Assumed parabolic.
‡ No associated comet known.

years after the comet disappeared. During all this time the earth and the comet had been playing tag; sometimes they nearly collided, but never quite succeeded. Between 1852 and 1885 the comet did not pass near Jupiter and its remains should have continued in the orbit they had in 1852. Any year we might have run into a dense swarm of meteors, but which year could not be foretold.

When darkness fell over Europe on November 27, 1872, faint meteors were pouring from the vicinity of Gamma Andromeda. For a few hours this cosmic blizzard increased in intensity, as Fig. 42 shows, until at 7:30 P.M. Greenwich time a single observer could

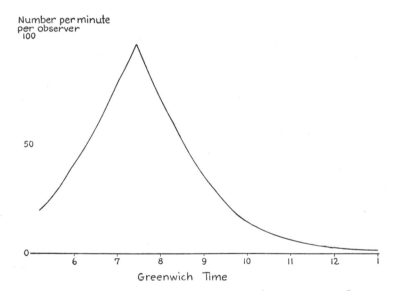

Fig. 42. Frequency of meteors in the great meteor shower of November 27, 1872. These meteors, originally part of Biela's comet, provided intense showers in 1872 and 1885. Since then they have shunned the earth.

see a hundred meteors a minute. After this peak the number decreased rapidly until by midnight only a few stragglers appeared. Observers in the Western Hemisphere saw only the end of the shower, but that was strong enough to attract attention. When this shower burst over the earth, the comet was many thousand kilometers away, for it had passed the junction of the orbits on September 9, 80 days before the earth arrived there. These meteors move in a short-period orbit of low inclination that brings them up behind the earth, so that they enter the atmosphere at a velocity of only 20 kilometers a second. That a majority of the meteors of the shower were faint is undoubtedly related to this fact; their average magnitude was about the third, while the Leonids and Perseids, coming head-on with higher velocity, average about the zero or first magnitude.

In 1878 the earth arrived a half-year before and in 1879 a half-year after the comet crossed the earth's orbit in mid-May 1879. Very few meteors were seen either year. After one more complete period the comet was due to pass its node again in mid-January 1886. On November 27, 1885 another celestial blizzard appeared and again European observers had the best show. The meteor frequency was almost identical with that in 1872 and the duration of the shower was also similar. Again the majority of the meteors were faint, although an occasional one was very bright. During this shower the first photograph of a meteor was secured by Weinek at Prague. We cannot tell precisely when these meteors moved out of the comet, but H. A. Newton thought the swarms we encountered in 1872 and 1885 started their independent careers in 1841, when the comet passed near Jupiter. This may be correct, but the shower of 1798 must have broken away earlier, possibly in 1772 when the comet probably also passed near Jupiter. Certainly the comet was at least a century in disintegrating so completely that it could no longer be seen. In 1890 and again in 1901 Jupiter exerted its influence upon the motions of the particles. A few members of this shower appeared in 1892 and in 1899, but since then we have had few traces of them. They continue to swing around the sun, passing the earth invisibly at a few million kilometers.

The Draconids

A modern counterpart of the Andromedes appeared on October 9, 1933. Again as dusk fell over Europe the sky was filled with faint meteors. Their numbers increased for only a short time, until at 8 P.M. Greenwich time 350 appeared each minute. Within an hour their frequency dropped to a tenth this maximum and before midnight, European time, when darkness came in America, the shower was over; Fig. 43 shows this brief maximum. The radiant point of these meteors was in the head of Draco, just where it should be if they were moving in the orbit of the short-period comet Giacobini-Zinner discovered in 1900.

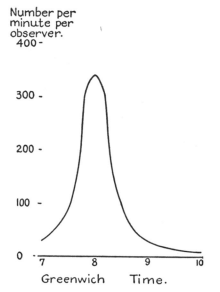

Fig. 43. *Frequency of meteors seen in the meteor shower of October 9, 1933. The meteors of this brief, but very intense, shower came from the short-period comet Giacobini-Zinner.*

This new shower–comet pair did not come as a complete surprise, for in 1926 Denning had seen enough meteors to reveal the radiant. Jupiter continued shifting the comet's orbit and decreased the clearance between it and earth's path, as Table 21 shows. In 1933 the earth passed through the junction of the orbits 80 days after the comet, which was then 230,000,000 kilometers away. Unlike Biela's comet, Giacobini's has not disappeared and we can observe what

Table 21. *Changes in the perihelion distance of Comet Giacobini-Zinner.*

Year	Perihelion distance (A.U.)
1900	0.9319
1913	.9759
1926	.9937
1933	.9997
1940	.9964
1946	.9956

orbital changes it undergoes as well as how it changes in appearance. Perhaps it will disappear, but the complete disruption of the comet is probably not imminent, even though meteors are scattered widely along its orbit (notice that Halley's comet is one of the brightest we know, yet each year we meet thousands of meteors moving along its orbit).

In 1940 comet Giacobini-Zinner crossed the earth's orbit on February 23. In 1939 the earth reached the intersection nearly a half-year early and in 1940 a half-year late; at neither time were any meteors seen from the shower radiant.

In 1946 the earth passed within 220,000 kilometers of the comet's orbit only 15 days after the comet had passed that point. A strong meteor shower appeared, which, if we make allowance for the bright moonlight, seems to have equaled that of 1933. Furthermore, the shower increased and diminished as rapidly as did the earlier display, despite the fact that the earth bored through the swarm closer to the parent comet. Most of the meteors had short paths and were faint. But some larger particles exist in the swarm, for several brilliant fireballs were seen. The yellowish color of the meteors agrees with Millman's report that the several dozen spectra he obtained show the yellow radiations from sodium as the strongest feature. A new high in meteor photography seems to have been set by Seyfert, who obtained 38 trails on the 12-minute exposure reproduced as Plate 26. Unless planetary perturbations divert the comet and attendant particles, strong showers may be expected to recur at 13-year intervals.

Over 200 Draconid trails were photographed by Millman from North Bay in Canada. Although clouds elsewhere prevented two-station photography, the velocity of the meteors is already accurately known from the comet orbit, which they closely follow. Unlike the Taurid, Geminid, and Leonid meteors, whose trails do not define a truly point radiant, the Draconids do have essentially a point radiant, indicating that they actually move in parallel orbits. Since these particles move in parallel paths very close to the comet orbit and are bunched near the comet, they represent quite early stages in the formation of a meteor stream. The abnormal height of first appearance, 97.7 kilometers for the average of the photographs, has led to the conclusion that the density of the particles is low, in fact, less than one. Inasmuch as these particles were until relatively recently part of comet Giacobini-Zinner, this low density for the particles supports Whipple's ice model of a comet.

On the afternoon of October 9, 1952 Lovell observed by radio techniques 60 meteors from this shower in 20 minutes. This group of particles were running 6 months ahead of the comet in their common orbit. Although no similar shower was observed in 1953, radio techniques will aid in revealing the rate at which the comet disintegrates.

The Taurids and Arietids

In 1940 Whipple found from five meteors photographed in duplicate that the Taurid meteors, which appear between October 14 and November 30, were associated with Encke's comet. Figure 44 shows

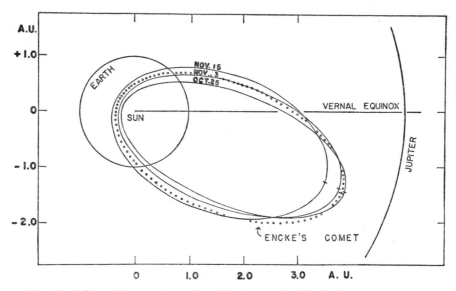

Fig. 44. Orbits of three northern Taurid meteors and of Encke's comet.

the similarities of the meteor and cometary orbits. Additional photographs have revealed two streams from Taurus and probably two others from neighboring Aries as a major organization within the interplanetary material. One Taurid stream has its radiant south of the ecliptic, while the other is nearby but north of the ecliptic.

These meteors are often bright despite their low atmospheric velocity, near 30 kilometers per second. The rarity of faint meteors from smaller particles hints that these particles separated from Encke's comet long ago. The considerable differences among the meteor orbits and between them and the comet orbit require perturbations operating over several thousands of years. Whipple estimated that one group of particles separated from the comet 5000 years ago and another group split off 1500 years ago. Especially interesting is the considerable range in perihelion distance of the meteors, from 0.24 to 0.46 A.U., which is associated with their dates of appearance and orbital orientations. Such a spread cannot arise from forces operating near perihelion. Searching for an explanation, Whipple has suggested that Encke's comet was once a great comet which collided with an asteroid outside the orbit of Mars. While some parts of the original comet may have been lost to the solar system, several fragments continue to move in orbits somewhat like that of the original comet. These fragments continually disperse at different rates to produce a vast assemblage of particles with some degree of concentration. Hamid pointed out that at least two of the strong daylight meteor showers recorded in the summer months by radio techniques (see Chapter 8) result from these Taurid meteors as they are moving away from the sun after perihelion passage.

Meteor Showers and Comets

The numerous agreements in Table 19 may suggest that each and every shower is known to be associated with a comet and similarly that every comet can provide a shower. On both aspects our observational data are incomplete. For example, on August 31, 1935 a brief but fairly intense shower radiated from Auriga, but no known periodic comet has a similar orbit. Probably the tiny swarm once belonged to a comet which disappeared a few centuries ago leaving remnants to continue moving around the sun like moths in the night.

The Geminid meteors of December are numerous each year, yet we cannot attribute them to any comet. Their short period, 1.65 years, and small perihelion distance, 0.14 A.U., derived by Whipple from Geminids photographed in duplicate, differ considerably from those of any comet known. Similarly, the Quadrantids, named for an

105

old constellation now included within Bootes, and the Delta Aquarids are other streams as yet unidentified with a comet; both have orbits with high inclination and short period. That comets moving in either of these short-period orbits have escaped detection seems highly improbable.

To show the large role that chance has played in these identifications we need only recount the circumstances by which the first three became possible. Precisely when the orbits of meteor showers were being determined, three faint comets appeared. The first of these, comet 1861 I — Lyrids — has a long-period orbit and will not be visible again for a century or more. Comet 1862 III — Perseids — also has a period exceeding a hundred years and will not return until the end of this century. Comet 1866 I — Leonids — has a period of 33 years, but in both 1899 and 1932 it was so situated in the sky that it could not be observed. Thus just at the most opportune moment these three comets appeared. If they had passed undiscovered then, we should be wondering whether the meteors that are widely spread over these long-period orbits had ever been associated with a comet and whether the comets still existed or were defunct. What odd conclusions we might have drawn regarding the origin and past history of these streams!

Table 20 sums up a century's accumulation of knowledge about meteor swarms. We find there the Bielid meteors, yet none have been observed since the start of this century. A similar list prepared in 1925 would not have included the Draconids, yet at the present moment they are one of the strongest and most interesting showers known. A few faint meteors from comet Pons-Winnecke were observed in 1916, 1921, and 1927, but there is little chance that we shall have a strong shower from this comet and it has not been included in this list.

When we consider the great number of comets that cross the earth's orbit, the number that supply meteor showers is small. None of the near-parabolic orbits have been identified with a shower, possibly because they are not frequently enough disturbed by solar heating to loosen up; or if they are, the particles become thinly spread around the vast orbit and are not recognized as a meteor shower. According to Fig. 28, the majority of periodic comets stay outside the earth's orbit and cannot supply us with meteors. Those that do cross the earth's orbit are, however, generous with their meteors. All these comets have short-period orbits that undergo many perturbations, and they are constantly disintegrating. Their low inclinations keep them near the earth's orbital plane, and as the particles spread out our chances of encountering at least some of the outriders of the swarms are increased.

Those showers selected for mention in Tables 13 and 20 are only the richer, more prominent ones. Dozens of weaker showers appear, but their reality is difficult to establish because the few meteors they provide are scrambled together in a hodgepodge of trails. The definitions and rules by which a real shower radiant can be identified have been the subject of much debate, but it is evident that the difficulties lie in distinguishing the shower radiant, found by projecting the trails backward until they cross, from an accidental grouping of the places at which other unrelated meteor trails cross. When an observer sees and imperfectly records three or four meteors of a weak shower among perhaps a hundred other meteors, he has great difficulty in making certain that the shower was real. As another complication, many showers catch up with the earth from behind, as do the short-period comets; therefore they have low velocities and their meteors are faint and infrequent. To circumvent some of these difficulties, Opik devised a statistical method by which he could evaluate the chance that any given set of meteors really composed a shower. From 2000 apparent radiants he selected 279 that were probably real. Of the 31 strongest showers included, 29 have orbits that bring them against the forward side of the earth. When, however, we derive parabolic orbits from the 279 radiants, we find that 65 percent of the showers came from behind the earth. The effects of velocity emphasize the streams meeting the earth head-on by making their meteors more numerous and brighter, but the great majority of the streams move in direct orbits of low inclination, as do the short-period comets with which they are probably associated.

The distances between the particles forming a meteor swarm are amazingly large and remind us of the small amount of material with which we are dealing. At the Perseid shower maximum, a single observer watching some 5000 square kilometers of atmosphere will see about one meteor per minute. Each of these meteors, weighing less than a gram, is the largest occupant of a space containing over

10,000,000 cubic kilometers. On the average, the particles are separated by over 200 kilometers. Similarly, H. A. Newton estimated that in the great Leonid shower of 1866 the particles were 30 kilometers apart. Within the densest part of the Bielid showers the particles averaged 40 kilometers apart. In contrast to these relatively dense clusters and streams, the average separation of sporadic meteors is about 500 kilometers.

The amount of material comprising all the meteors scattered around the Perseid orbit can be estimated crudely. Let us assume that for one full day the Perseids appear at their maximum rate and that each particle weighs 25 milligrams. The total amount of material scattered along the orbit comes out as about 500,000,000 tons, which would make a layer 2 centimeters thick over the state of Connecticut. This is then a minimum value for the mass of the comet before the meteors began to scatter around its path; the actual mass may have been many times as much.

Formation of Meteor Streams

One point about the evolution of a meteor stream seems to be clear. At first the meteors are in swarms close to or part of the parent comet. As planetary perturbations gradually influence their period, they stray away, moving in practically the same orbit as the comet but running ahead or behind. Given sufficient time they become uniformly distributed around the orbit. The Perseids seem to represent the full development of this process which, owing to their high orbital inclination, has proceeded without recent serious planetary influences. The slowly acting influences of planetary attractions, which have gradually tilted the orbits of comet 1862 III and the Perseids, have been computed backward by Hamid. He found that the greatest opportunity for the comet to have been thrown into its present orbit came through a fairly close approach to Jupiter 343 revolutions, some 40,000 years, ago. During this long interval the broad and uniformly dispersed meteor stream has gradually developed.

Meteor streams from short-period comets, which have low orbital inclinations and frequent planetary disturbances, spread out more rapidly and become increasingly difficult to recognize. According to the photographic evidence, the number of days during which a shower is observable seems to be related to the size of the radiant area. This scatter in individual radiant points arises from the differences in the orbits of the separate particles and indicates the degree to which the initially compact swarms have dispersed. The Draconids, visible for only a few hours, radiate from an area having a radius not larger than 3′; the Leonids during 6 days have a radiant 13′ in radius; while the Northern Taurids, observed for 46 days, have a radiant 61′ in radius. The widely dispersed Taurid streams probably represent about the thinnest groupings that can be identified with a comet. Not only are the particles fairly evenly distributed around their orbit, but they have undergone so many planetary perturbations that their orbits differ appreciably from that of the parent comet.

The particles from many comets have been dispersed through such a large volume that we seldom encounter enough to make a recognizable shower. The Andromedes from Biela's comet are going through the same process, but they still travel as small clusters only a few hundred thousand kilometers across. The chances that the earth will encounter a swarm of this size are very small, and many such swarms must move between the planets and remain unknown to us until by accident the earth meets them.

In the previous chapter we considered how the velocity of a meteor influenced its brightness and observability. Within a shower all the velocities are equal and the distribution of magnitudes indicates the number of particles of different sizes. Over a range of eight magnitudes the frequency of Draconid meteors seemed to increase uniformly 2.5 times with each magnitude. The eight magnitudes are equivalent to a range of a thousand in the masses of the particles, or a factor of ten in their diameters. In the Leonid and Perseid showers, faint meteors, especially those detected only through binoculars or a telescope, or by radio, are rare; the same is true for the Geminids. These streams seem to contain few small particles. Large particles also are rare among the shower meteors, which seldom present us with a tremendous fireball. Furthermore, no meteorite has been identified as coming from any known shower.

We have then what seems good evidence that the particles are being sorted according to their sizes and that only those of comparable size move together. This effect cannot be attributed to the radiation pressure of sunlight, for that is ineffective with particles of this size. Collisions between large and small bodies in a swarm or with stray bodies moving through space will change the motions of the small bodies more than the large ones, but such collisions will be rare when the tiny particles are separated by hundreds of kilometers. A more effective means of winnowing out the small particles comes through the Poynting-Robertson effect found in the theory of relativity. All of the particles are illuminated by sunlight. As they become warm, they reradiate heat into space in all directions. But the radiation in the direction of the particle's motion pushes back on it more strongly, thereby retarding its motion; furthermore, small particles are retarded most rapidly. Since a change in velocity results in a change in orbit, within a few thousand years the smaller members of a stream move quite differently from the larger bodies. We have then a stratification or segregation according to size, which combines with the other effects operating to dissipate meteor swarms.

These small particles from meteor streams spiral toward and eventually into the sun along orbits of diminishing size and eccentricity. Not only is this effect important in scattering particles from meteor streams; it operates to eliminate any small bodies within the solar system. A particle 0.1 centimeter across moving like a typical asteroid will in only 60,000,000 years have spiraled into the sun. In 4,000,000,000 years, approximately the age of the earth, particles with diameters as large as about 10 centimeters would be removed from the inner parts of the solar system, swallowed by the sun. Furthermore, such large particles are ground up by frequent collisions with the more numerous smaller bodies. The current existence of particles 1 centimeter or less in diameter leads us to conclude that until relatively recently they were part of some larger body, either a comet or an asteroid.

Radio Writes a Record

Radio and radar have become new tools for astronomical research. Especially in the study of meteors these new devices are providing much accurate information and some that could not be obtained by any other means. As early as 1931 there were suggestions from both sides of the Atlantic that certain types of peculiar radio signals might be due to reflections of radio waves from small clouds of ions produced by meteors. Simultaneous visual and radio observations of the Leonid showers in 1931 and 1932 revealed a reasonable number of coincidences between the appearance of bright meteors and the peculiar signals. While interesting, these conclusions appeared to offer little promise for a new field of investigation, and few follow-up studies were made. However, in 1938 J. A. Pierce, using pulsed signals to study the ionosphere, or "radio roof," obtained sufficient evidence to suggest that important new information on meteors could be obtained through the use of radio equipment. The advent of World War II diverted attention from this and many other promising lines of research, but the wartime development of powerful radio equipment, and especially of high-frequency pulsing equipment (radar) for detection of aircraft and ships through echoes of radio signals, has provided very useful tools.

An additional method of detecting meteors by radio was discovered in 1941 by Chamanlal and Venkataraman in India while listening to a high-frequency broadcast station a few miles away. Occasionally the program was interrupted by brief "whistles" which usually fell in pitch. Their search for an explanation of this phenomenon led them to consider meteors as a possible cause. Visual observations of meteors showed many coincidences between the appearance of bright meteors and the whistles. Since 1945, echoes, observed both with radar, presenting range-time information, and as whistles, providing intensity-time information, have permitted round-the-clock meteor studies in fair weather and foul. Observations with radio waves of different lengths, between 3 and 150 meters, and ingenious arrangements of the antennas provide a wide assortment of information for comparative studies.

Since radar observations do not seem to be altered or invalidated by the presence of sunlight, they can be used to provide continuous information on meteor frequency throughout both day and night. Figure 45 presents the hourly meteor rates observed on a wavelength of 11 meters during 11 months of continuous recording at the U. S. National Bureau of Standards. For reference the approximate dark intervals during which visual observations could be made have also been indicated for latitude 40°N. For most of the months the daily variations in frequency exhibit a maximum before 6 A.M., when the apex of the earth's motion is high in the sky, and a minimum around 6 P.M. (18 hours) when the antiapex is high. The months of May, June, and July show, however, high counts with the maximum meteor frequency developing at or continuing after 6 A.M.; this daytime activity was first noted in 1946 by Hey and Stewart. Obviously, this activity during daylight could never be detected from visual observations. As discussed below, these high meteor rates after sunrise are evidence of relative strong showers striking the earth while the particles are moving away from perihelion.

The average of these hourly rates over the 11-month observing period, also presented in Fig. 45, shows a threefold change in rate between the evening minimum and the morning maximum. According to visual and photographic observations the change in rate between evening and morning is about four times. Such differences remind us that much remains to be learned about the selection effects operating upon radar observations and the over-all correspondence between visual and photographic meteor observations and those made with radio devices.

Radar Observations

A radar set sends out on very short wavelengths a continuous series of brief, but powerful, radio signals called pulses, each of which lasts only a few millionths of a second. Between pulses, while the transmitter is "off," the radio signals, traveling at 300,000 kilo-

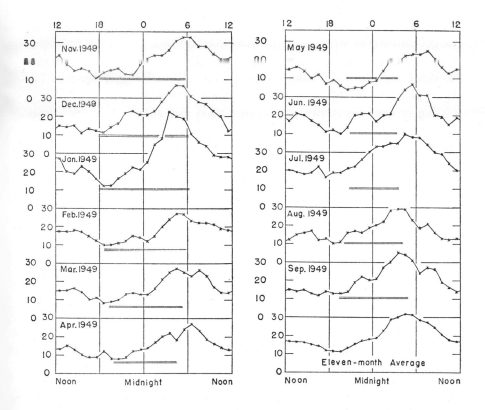

Fig. 45. *Average hourly meteor rates recorded with radar throughout 11 months. These meteor rates were recorded with continuously operating constant-power radar equipment at the U. S. National Bureau of Standards. The double horizontal lines indicate the hours during which visual meteor observations would have been possible at latitude 40° N.*

113

meters per second, may go several hundred kilometers, be echoed back from a "target," and return to the receiver before the next pulse is emitted. To provide an echo the target must be at least as large as the wavelength of the radiation striking it; long waves will be bounced back only from large targets. Hence it might seem that very short radio waves would be the most useful for meteor study. But short waves are returned only from dense ion clouds and will go through thin ones. We see therefore that radio waves of various wavelengths can provide different types of information. Furthermore, whether or not an echo can be detected depends upon the strength of the echo, which is proportional to the effective area of the target and to the square of the wavelength used. Radar observations show that both the number and the duration of echoes from meteors increase rapidly with longer wavelengths. Usually wavelengths between 5 and 50 meters are used for meteor studies.

The type of transmitting antenna used determines in what directions the signals go and how broad or narrow a beam they form. The signal from a simple half-wave dipole antenna will floodlight most of the sky. More elaborate antennas, which are more readily constructed for short wavelengths than for long, will focus the signals into a beam or a fan covering a small sector of the sky. Various types of antennas are useful, since they provide different types of information.

The very weak echoes returned from distant targets are amplified and then displayed in various forms on the face of a cathode-ray tube somewhat similar to that used in a television set. Visual observation can be made of the echo "pips" appearing on the cathode-ray tube, but this is monotonous work requiring the continuous services of an alert observer. Automatic photography has replaced visual recording because it provides a permanent record that can be examined at leisure and measured with care.

The range, or distance to the target, is proportional to the time interval between transmission and return of the signal. In meteor studies the uncertainty in radar range is usually about 1 kilometer, but in some equipment it has been reduced to about 0.1 kilometer.

The type of range record to be expected from an ion cloud moving with the velocity of the meteor is shown in Fig. 46. The diagram on the left represents the path of the meteor, with equi-

spaced time marks shown along the path. On the right is the magnified relation between time and range as it would be shown on the
cathode-ray tube. As the meteor moves closer to the radio equipment, the range diminishes and the trace descends. When the
meteor passes broadside, the range reaches a minimum. Thereafter,
as the meteor moves away, the range increases. For a meteor moving
with uniform velocity, the record of the relation between time and
range forms a hyperbola and appears as part or all of a J- or U-shaped
pattern. If the meteor is decelerated, the observed record will depart
from the hyperbolic curve.

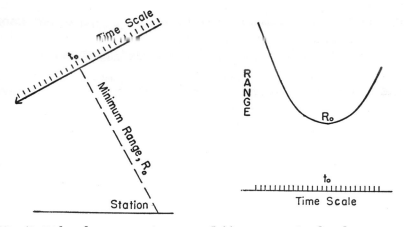

Fig. 46. Radar observations of meteors: (left) geometry of radar observation of a
meteor, with equispaced time scale along meteor path; (right) range-time record obtained for such a meteor.

The rapidity with which information can be accumulated from
radio observations is indicated by the results obtained in less than
two years of intermittent operation by Millman and McKinley in
Canada: 50,000 photographic recordings of "whistles" and 1,500,000
photographic records of radar echoes. Similarly, Pineo, using somewhat lower power at the U. S. Bureau of Standards, obtained 62,000
photographic records of radar echoes in eight months of continuous
recording. The careful analysis of even a fraction of this quantity of
information is an almost overwhelming task.

The discussion in previous chapters of what is known about meteor
trails, spectra, and trains provides a basis for interpreting the various
types of echo phenomena observed with radar equipment. Around

the path of the tiny solid particle producing the observable meteor as it plunges through the atmosphere there forms an advancing column of hot, partially ionized gas hardly more than a few meters in diameter, with a temperature of several thousand degrees. From these expanding ionized gases radio echoes provide a variety of records, some of which are rather complex, as illustrated in Plate 28. Those investigating these records in a relatively new and rapidly developing field of research are cautious about asserting that a particular type of record should be specifically identified with a particular phase of the meteor-forming activity. They realize that the front of the ion column extends forward at a velocity equal to that of the meteor. On some records, especially those obtained with short waves, an echo of short duration shows as a J- or U-shaped curve that develops with the velocity of the meteor particle. This has been termed the head echo, but the mechanism of its origin is not clearly understood. In the great majority of cases the observed meteor echo comes, however, from the ionized column left behind. These echoes are strongest when the column is broadside to the line of sight and most of the meteors are detected when seen broadside and not changing rapidly in range.

After the meteor has passed, the column of ionization expands and diffuses; correspondingly, the sensitivity of the equipment to the broadside aspect decreases. In many cases on wavelengths greater than 6 meters echoes do not appear for as long as several seconds after the visual meteor has vanished. The duration of echoes from these large expanding ion clouds is much greater when relatively long wavelengths are used. For meteors moving in the line of sight, or nearly head-on, echoes from such enduring ion clouds are often the only records obtained. Such clouds often persist for many seconds, may break into several components at different ranges (heights), and sometimes drift in range. For bright shower meteors the duration of these secondary ion clouds has been found to be proportional to the duration of the visual train. Since both radar and visual trains appear at approximately the same heights, some physical association seems probable. Yet the mechanism by which either the enduring meteor train or the enduring radar echo is produced and maintained for such relatively long intervals is not yet fully understood.

The influence of a heavy meteor shower upon the ionosphere can be seen in Plate 29, which presents the record obtained with waves of 86-meter wavelength by Pierce at Harvard during the 1946 shower of Draconid meteors. Normally at night the 86-meter waves used by Pierce penetrate the lower, or E, region of the ionosphere and are reflected from the higher and more strongly ionized F region. During this shower the meteors appeared so frequently at about the normal height of the E region that a pseudo E layer was present. Over 4000 individual meteor echoes must have been contributed to this single record; furthermore, the maximum frequency of appearance on this record agrees within a few minutes with the time of maximum determined by visual observation elsewhere where the skies were clear. During this Draconid shower on October 9 10, 1946, Hey, in England, using a wavelength of 4 meters, also obtained meteor echoes. Under normal conditions not more than two meteor echoes per hour were observed, but during this intense shower the rate rose to a brief maximum of 168 per minute, equal to 10,000 per hour. According to one report, similar radar observations of the Draconid shower were made in the Soviet Union.

Velocities for individual meteors can be found from the change of range with time. Before this velocity relative to the observing station can be transformed into a heliocentric velocity, the location of the path through the atmosphere must be found. Millman and McKinley in Canada, from the records obtained at three separate radar stations near Ottawa, have derived the path, velocity, and orbit for a bright sporadic meteor moving nearly horizontally, recorded at 6 P.M. on August 4, 1948. These records are reproduced in Plate 30. The velocity in the atmosphere was 35.0 kilometers per second. On the radar records the meteor appeared at a height of 108 kilometers and disappeared at a height of 104 kilometers. Its heliocentric velocity was 37.6 kilometers per second, well below the parabolic limit. The most reasonable orbit, in view of small uncertainties in the observations, had a semimajor axis of 2.7 A.U., a period of 4.4 years, an eccentricity of 0.87, and an inclination of 34°. This orbit resembles those of the asteroids that come near the earth. Since the number of meteors recorded by radio is very high, many exceptionally good records are available for detailed study. Certainly radar observations can be far more precise than those obtained visually. In

117

a few cases, when the definition of the radar range-time record has been exceptionally good, the deceleration of the meteors has been determined; this is then used to yield information about the density of the atmosphere at high altitudes.

From duplicate radar ranges the heights of meteors can be determined with an uncertainty of about 1 kilometer. In Canada, simultaneous visual and radar observations of Perseid meteors indicate that for this shower, at least, visual observations reveal the meteors at higher altitudes than do the radar observations. These observations also confirm the photographic evidence that the slower meteors have lower mean heights. For example, the mean height of Geminids was 97.0 kilometers, while that of Perseids was 102.6 kilometers. That the mean height of August non-Perseids was 97.1 kilometers suggests that their average velocity in the atmosphere was less than that of the Perseids and close to the velocity of the Geminids. This inference about average meteor velocities is confirmed by McKinley's velocity determinations from "whistles" reported below.

By averaging numerous individual velocities of modest precision obtained through other radar techniques, velocities with uncertainties less than 1 kilometer per second have been obtained for some of the showers whose velocities are already known from orbital or photographic evidence. Such calibration is always essential when a new tool or method comes into use. The results show no systematic differences from the results obtained by other reliable methods. We may, therefore, accept similar radar velocities and orbits derived for other showers whose orbits have previously been poorly determined.

Daytime Showers

In 1947 Lovell, Clegg, and others at Manchester, England, began systematic investigation of Hey's earlier discovery that during the summer months strong meteor showers occurred during the daylight hours before noon. During the intervening years, improvements in equipment and technique have slightly modified the first conclusions while they have increasingly emphasized the fact that of the annual meteor phenomena these daylight showers are among the strongest.

Radiants have been located by several ingenious procedures based on the fact that with wavelengths of 4 to 5 meters meteors are rarely detected except when their paths are broadside to the transmitted signal. The radiant is then 90° from the center of the transmitted beam. Two beams, perhaps 15° wide, or two narrow fans are radiated in different directions from two antennas. As a radiant moves through a position nearly 90° from the beams, the meteor frequency rises rapidly, then falls. From two such observations in different directions, the radiant can be located with an uncertainty of only 1° or 2°. Another technique of comparable precision is based upon the decrease in range of the echoes as the radiant approaches a position 90° from the beam.

In 1949, following earlier confirmatory and exploratory work and equipmental improvement, intensive study was begun. Between May and August a sizable number of radiant areas extending from Aquarius to Taurus and Perseus were isolated. Continued observations in 1950 and 1951 did not confirm all of these as annual radiants, but some year-to-year variation in the activity of various radiants must be expected. In addition, the radar equipment permits only strong radiants to be recognized. What at first seemed to be a great multiplicity of individual radiant points, seems rather to result from four major and quite diffuse meteor streams appearing annually plus some others that are active only in occasional years. Since these meteors are moving away from perihelion and appear on the sunlit side of the earth, without the radio observations we would never have known of these showers, which are at least as strong as any of the annual nighttime showers. Each of the new showers has been named from some star near the radiant. The known characteristics of these four annual showers are summarized in Table 22. The ve-

Table 22. Annual daytime meteor streams.

| Stream | Date | | Maximum frequency per hour [*] | Radiant, mean date | | Velocity (km/sec) | |
	Mean	Maximum		R.A. (deg)	Dec. (deg)	Observed	Heliocentric
o — Cetids	May 19	May 21	22	29	−3	36.7±4.2	32.5±2.7
Arietids	June 8	June 8	60	44	+24	37.7±4.3	34.0±2.9
ζ — Perseids	June 6	June 4	40	62	+24	28.8±3.2	34.8±2.0
β — Taurids	June 30	July 2	30	86	+19	31.4±4.1	36.7±2.8

[*] As observed with the Manchester radio equipment the background of meteors not belonging to these showers increased from around 15 per hour in May to 25 per hour in July.

locities reported are averages for groups; while they lack the precision of velocities obtained photographically, within narrow limits they define the orbits given in Table 23. The greatest uncertainty is in the orbital size and period, but all four orbits have periods of at most a few years, similar to those of the Geminids and the Taurids.

Table 23. Orbits of daytime meteor streams.

Stream	ω (deg)	Ω (deg)	i (deg)	e	a (A.U.)	q (A.U.)	P (approx.) (yr)
o — Cetids	211±3	238	34±7	0.91	1.3±0.4	0.11	1.5
Arietids	29±2	77	18±5	.94	1.5±0.7	.10	1.8
ζ — Perseids	61±4	77	4±2	.79	1.7±0.5	.35	2.2
β — Taurids	244±4	278	6±3	.85	1.4 to 5.3	.34	3.3

As early as 1940 Whipple noted that the inclination of the Taurid streams was so low that the earth might encounter them a second time as the particles moved away from perihelion. The daytime β-Taurids may be a return of the nighttime Northern Taurids, while the daytime ζ-Perseids may be a second encounter with the Southern Arietids. Because the streams are diffuse and the radar observations are of lower precision than the photographic, these identifications are best considered as probable. Especially interesting is the geometry of the two possible contacts between the earth and the Taurid streams (Fig. 44). The displacement of the radiant positions due to the earth's orbital motion causes the apparent radiant both before and after perihelion passage to lie in the same constellation, Taurus.

The daytime Arietids have an orbit similar to that of the δ-Aquarids. While the orbits are not identical, the two streams may have had a common origin in the past.

For two of the showers not observed each year Ellyett and Davis derived velocities. The 54-Perseids had an observed velocity of 37.5 ± 3.7 kilometers per second, which gives a heliocentric velocity of 39.1 ± 2.6 kilometers per second, while the θ-Aurigids had an observed velocity of 32.9 ± 2.7 kilometers per second and a corresponding heliocentric velocity of only 27.5 ± 1.4 kilometers per second. If this last velocity is correct, the length of the semimajor axis of the orbit of the θ-Aurigids is only 0.8 A.U. and their period is less than a year, which is the shortest period known for a meteor stream. Since such a stream is always fairly near the sun, we may conclude that it is disintegrating rapidly and must have originated recently.

Observations of "Whistles"

The whistle, or intensity-time, phenomenon discovered in 1941 by Chamanlal and Venkataraman can be observed from effects upon both pulse and continuous-wave radio transmission. These techniques yield a thousand times as many records as do range-time techniques. When the path of a meteor can be defined from visual or radar data, the whistles, recorded photographically for detailed study, provide accurate meteor velocities. Ellyett and Davies in England, a group of investigators at Stanford University, and McKinley in Canada have pioneered in this technique.

McKinley has determined velocities for 10,933 meteors from records selected as the best from many more obtained during 850 hours of operation between December 1948 and March 1950. Although his equipment would reveal velocities up to 150 kilometers per second, the observed geocentric velocities ranged only between 12 and 80 kilometers per second, as shown in Fig. 47. Only 0.3 percent of the velocities, determined with an accuracy of about 5 percent, were between 75 and 80 kilometers per second and none exceeded 80 kilometers per second. McKinley interpreted these results as demonstrating that all, or nearly all, meteors down to the eighth or ninth magnitudes as detected by his equipment are moving with less than parabolic velocity, have elliptic orbits, and are members of the solar system. Similarly, but from fewer records, British workers found no clearly hyperbolic velocities. Thus radio observations have provided an answer to a vexing problem in meteor study.

The implications of this result for cosmogony, which is the study of the structure and history of the universe, are important. Meteor photography had already indicated that few if any bright meteors come from outside the solar system. Now radio records, including meteors bright enough to be photographed, those observed visually, and others in the telescopic class, indicate that fewer than 1 percent of the particles having masses greater than around 1 milligram come from outside the solar system. While such particles may exist in interstellar space, they must be widely separated and make no appreciable contribution to the earth's present rate of meteoric accretion.

The rate at which the ion cloud formed by a meteor drifts has been studied by the group at Stanford University through other phenomena associated with the whistles. Most of these electrified clouds

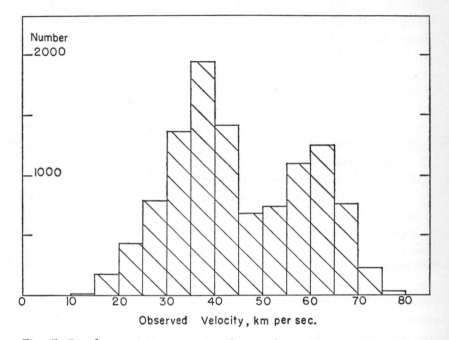

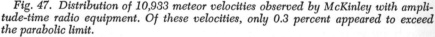

Fig. 47. *Distribution of 10,933 meteor velocities observed by McKinley with amplitude-time radio equipment. Of these velocities, only 0.3 percent appeared to exceed the parabolic limit.*

seem to move horizontally and not to be guided by the earth's magnetic field. From about two dozen cases the drift velocities were found to be between 50 and 200 kilometers per hour, with the greatest frequency between 100 and 150 kilometers per hour. Some peculiar results suggest that the winds at high altitudes blow in different directions in adjacent layers. This is consistent with the considerable drift and deformation observed visually and photographically in meteor trains, which sometimes curl into odd shapes within a few minutes after being formed.

The discovery that meteors could be detected and studied by

means of various radio devices has opened up a whole new field of research to supplement the techniques previously in use. Meteor frequencies, heights, radiant points, velocities, and orbits can be obtained from radio signals irrespective of the time of day or the weather. In addition, these investigations are supplying much new information about the structure and physical processes present in the upper atmosphere. These new lines of evidence are providing more complete knowledge of the earth's shielding envelope and of the particles that dash into it.

☆
☆ **9** ☆

A Meteorite Falls

A great fireball abruptly flaring into view may not be completely consumed in its mad dash through the atmosphere; sometimes a remnant falls to the earth below. These chunks of stone and metal, the *meteorites*, are the only solid material from outer space that we can study in our laboratories. Through careful study of how they reached the earth and of their composition and structure we may be able to learn what types of material move between the planets and what their past history has been.

Only a few new meteorites are recognized each year, but the total known is over 1400. Each is identified by the name of the nearest town or prominent landmark, thus establishing the place of discovery as well as the identity. Since meteorites are found in all parts of the world, their names constitute a veritable geography lesson, including Joe Wright Mountain (Arkansas), Willy Willy (Australia), Bustee (India), and Prambachkirchen (Austria).

New meteorites are recognized through two processes; some are seen to fall and are immediately recovered, while others are accidentally found and subsequently recognized as meteorites. In statistical discussions these two modes of discovery must be carefully distinguished. On the basis of composition, meteorites can be divided into three groups — those composed of metal, those of stone, and more rarely those of the two materials in roughly equal proportion. The dense metallic masses, composed principally of nickel and iron, immediately reveal themselves as unusual material wherever found. In contrast the stony masses, differing but little from ordinary rocks in density and appearance, pass unnoticed upon casual inspection. From Table 24 we see that among found meteorites the great majority are metallic, or *irons*, while among the witnessed falls *stones*

Table 24. *Frequency of meteorite finds and falls.*

Type	Finds		Falls	
	Number	Percent	Number	Percent
Irons	409	66	29	5
Stony-irons	46	7½	8	1½
Stones	165	26½	547	93½
Total	620		584	

predominate by ten to one. In regions where a dense population has existed for a long time, the fraction of irons among the total meteorites is low, for those that fell centuries ago have been collected and turned into implements. The proportion of irons in India is only 3 percent, in Japan 12 percent, and in Europe 14 percent. Over recently settled areas the fraction of irons runs much higher; for North America it is 69 percent and for Australia 81 percent. Arid regions devoid of trees and undergrowth favor the preservation and later discovery of metallic meteorites, for rusting and disintegration proceed there at a minimum rate. Of 111 meteorites from India 108 were seen to fall, while of 43 from Chile not one was witnessed!

When Meteorites Hit the Earth

Our astronomical information about meteorites from fireballs is very poor, which is hardly surprising since we must depend upon the observations of untrained people who are startled by the unheralded apparition. Velocities have been derived for a few fireballs that produced meteorites, but the results obtained, like those for fireballs in general, are of questionable accuracy. For the seemingly well-observed Pultusk stones, which fell in Poland on January 30, 1868, Galle derived a heliocentric velocity considerably greater than the parabolic limit. The body caught up with the earth from behind and entered the atmosphere with nearly its minimum possible velocity.

Yet the derived beginning height of 280 kilometers is improbably large and recalls the stretching effect that probably distorts the velocities derived for fireballs from reports of inexperienced observers. Wylie has derived paths and orbits for three typical stony meteorites, Tilden, Paragould and Archie. These move around the sun in orbits with periods of 2 to 4 years, low inclinations, and eccentricities near 0.5. These orbits resemble those of some asteroids.

Unfortunately, there seem to be no indisputable velocity observations on a falling meteorite. Perhaps the several continuously operated radar stations will provide such a record. Yet there is almost unanimous agreement that meteorites have been permanent members of the solar system. This conclusion is based upon circumstantial evidence from the photographically determined velocities for bright meteors, which are only slightly smaller bodies than meteorites. Also, the internal structures of the meteorites themselves present many lines of evidence which seem to require them to have been permanently part of the solar system.

From the radiant points of fireballs that dropped meteorites some information about their orbits can be found. From 116 cases H. A. Newton concluded that the great majority of meteorites overtook the earth in direct orbits of low inclination and large perihelion distance. In such orbits the meteorites enter the atmosphere with very low velocities, which minimizes their chances of being disrupted. A few meteorites do survive head-on collision with the earth, but usually at the cost of being shattered into thousands of fragments. In several cases, such as the Plainview meteorite (Plate 31), some of the fragments can be fitted together to form a single mass.

According to Fig. 48, meteorite falls are observed most frequently in the afternoon and during the summer months. The predominance of afternoon over morning falls is probably significant, for in the afternoon the point in space from which the earth is moving as it goes around the sun is above the horizon. W. J. Fisher showed that more falls are observed in daytime than in nighttime and in summer than in winter because the falling material is seen or the dust it raises at impact attracts attention. At night, when fireballs are most conspicuous, meteorites are rarely recovered unless they happen to strike buildings; a few such cases are known. In 1847 one of the Braunau irons, weighing 21 kilograms, fell through a bedroom, without harming the three children sleeping there. Incidentally, there are no verified cases on record of people having been killed by falling meteorites. There are, however, some records of people having been struck by fragments. In November 1954 a woman in Alabama was bruised and startled when a small stony meteorite fell through the roof of her house and struck her.

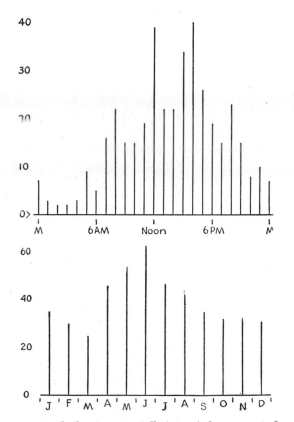

Fig. 48. The times at which meteorites fall: (upper) the times of observed meteorite falls according to the hour of the day; the maximum rate is in mid-afternoon; (lower) the times of observed meteorite falls according to month; the maximum rate is closely associated with the duration of daylight in the Northern Hemisphere.

It is difficult to associate a meteorite falling during the afternoon with the strong meteor showers that appear late at night; we know of no meteorite that has fallen from a meteor shower. Although many meteorites overtake the earth, as do many weak meteor show-

127

ers, what, if any, relation there is between the two will become clearer when we have better velocities and orbits for the meteorites. Photographic or radar observations, although covering only a small fraction of the sky, may eventually record a meteorite's fall.

During recent decades the number of meteorite discoveries has increased rapidly (Fig. 49); at present the rate averages 25 a year.

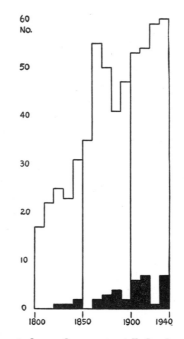

Fig. 49. The frequency of observed meteorite falls by decades. Since 1800 the num- ber of observed meteorite falls has constantly increased as people became more "me- teorite conscious." The solid area represents metallic meteorites while the light area represents stony meteorites.

Such a rate has, however, not been steady in the past. Occasionally one or more years have passed without the discovery of a single new meteorite; only one new meteorite was reported in each of the four consecutive years 1906, 1907, 1908, and 1909. A precise count of the meteorites known at any time is difficult to obtain. New bodies may be discovered but not recognized or reported for several years; also, what appears to be two different but adjacent meteorites may, after careful study, be assigned to the same parent mass. The present high rate of discovery indicates an increased interest in meteorites; people are becoming meteorite conscious.

In the United States many of the current discoveries result from the efforts of the Meteoritical Society. H. H. Nininger, a modern pioneer in locating meteorites, has also been outstandingly successful because he has toured the midwestern plains states lecturing about and exhibiting meteorites. Through these efforts many old as well as freshly fallen specimens have been recognized. For several years Nininger was accounting for half of all discoveries in the world. In 1937 he added 31 new meteorites to the list.

As soon as a great detonating fireball that seems likely to have dropped meteorites is reported, investigators travel to the region and interview the observers. Their reports define the probable fall area, which is then surveyed with the aid of the local inhabitants, who continue to watch for specimens. Through this procedure several freshly fallen meteorites have been recovered in spite of the fact that they fell after dark at some distance from any observer. The fruitfulness of the plains regions can be appreciated by comparing its stonefree, widely cultivated soil with the rocky, wooded hillsides of New England, from which only six meteorites, all but one being witnessed falls, have been collected.

Piercing the Atmosphere

When meteorites dash into the earth's atmosphere they move faster than the air molecules. As a result, the air is trapped and greatly compressed in front of the cosmic plunger. Such a cap of compressed air becomes intensely hot and melts the surface material of the meteorite. In the air stream this liquid is continually swept away, the droplets appearing as sparks. As these fireballs blaze into the lower part of the atmosphere they produce intense detonations, which sound from nearby like the sharp crack of cannon fire and from afar like the distant roll of thunder. When the velocity of the meteorite has been greatly reduced through friction, the hot air cap is no longer maintained, the fireball dies out, and the liquid freezes into a dark crust. For stony material the crust is a real glass, but for the metallic stuffs it is of iron and nickel oxides as smooth as glass. Some meteorites, like the Lafayette stone shown in Plate 32, are shaped like blunt cones with flow marks radiating from the apex while the flat base seems to have been protected from the air blast. Evidently these blocks kept the same side forward during flight and were carved by the air into their conical form. The nonconical meteorites have a great variety of forms and probably have spun over and over as they fell.

Under the high pressure of the compressed-air cap many stony meteorites shatter. Instead, then, of a single mass reaching the earth a great shower of particles of various sizes is sprayed over an area that covers many square kilometers. Thousands of fragments, down to the size of a pea, were collected from an area 5 kilometers long and 1 kilometer wide under the Holbrook, Arizona meteor of July 19, 1912. Ordinarily the long axis of such an area closely parallels the motion of the meteor and the largest masses lie at the end toward which the meteor moved. Iron meteorites sometimes fall in several pieces, but usually their toughness enables them to withstand the hazards of flight through the atmosphere. In contrast, only rarely is a single stone collected that appears to constitute the total fall. Nininger reports cases like the Pasamonte meteor of March 24, 1933, where for kilometers along under the path of a stony meteorite fine gravelly particles fell.

When a meteorite has been so retarded that the cap of hot air dissipates, the fireball vanishes and the dark body falls as though released from an airplane. Large meteorites strike the ground with such force that they bury themselves to considerable depths. The 43-kilogram Hraschina iron plunged a meter into a recently plowed field. During ancient times many large meteorites, especially the irons, buried themselves deeply in the soft subsoil and there they stayed, like the Hugoton stone shown in Plate 33, until they disintegrated or, as the overlying material eroded away, a plow struck them. More than 5 percent of discovered meteorites have been unearthed in the course of excavations, some lying as deep as 6 meters. A vast number of such undiscovered bodies, similar to the one shown in Plate 34, must lie beneath our feet.

Various electric and magnetic devices, like mine detectors, have been made and tested for locating buried meteorites. One of the most effective was made by La Paz and used in his survey of the Odessa meteor crater. With this device he located meteorites to depths exceeding a meter. The meteorites that he located within 12 hours and excavated during a survey of this crater made the large collection shown in Plate 35.

Early in the morning of February 18, 1948 the largest stony meteorite known fell near Norton, Kansas. The meteorite burst twice, at altitudes of 40 and 18 kilometers, and left a dust cloud visible for 2 hours. From reports of observers the probable fall area was defined; later many fragments were found on both sides of the Kansas-Nebraska state line. In August 1948 the largest mass, weighing about a ton, was found in a hole 2 meters wide and 2 meters deep to the upper surface of the body. It is a conical mass of a relatively rare achondritic type which was buried with the nose at a depth of 3 meters.

Whether swarms of separate metallic masses enter the atmosphere is of interest but is difficult to determine. Spencer suspected that the many large Bethany irons found in Southwest Africa fell at the same time. Henderson, from new chemical analyses, found that the numerous hexahedrite irons from northern Chile are remarkably similar and has suggested that they may have fallen together. As both the Bethany and the Chilean masses were scattered over large areas, they may have formed loose clusters before entering the earth's atmosphere.

Temperatures of Meteorites

One common misconception about meteorites involves their temperatures both before they encounter the earth and as they fall through the atmosphere. In Chapter 1 we reviewed the temperatures that bodies have at various solar distances and depicted these in Fig. 3. Furthermore, the time intervals represented in Fig. 4 for parabolic orbits are the least times that bodies will spend moving from one temperature region to another. Since, even in parabolic orbits, the bodies require several days to move between regions whose black-body temperatures differ by 10°, their temperatures will be near those indicated in Fig. 3. Before they enter the earth's atmosphere, metallic bodies, which have high heat conductivity, will have temperatures near 4°C (277°K). Stony meteorites, through which temperature changes are slower, may be somewhat warmer or colder, depending upon whether they are leaving or approaching the vicinity of the sun. But even at the center of a stony body several feet in diameter, the temperature will not be many degrees above or below 4°C

As the bodies dash through the atmosphere a thin outer layer is liquefied by the rapid rise in temperature; this liquid is immediately swept away and a fresh cool layer of material exposed. During the air flight, which lasts only a few seconds, the heat from the surface material has little opportunity to leak inward. Freshly fallen irons are generally just too hot to handle comfortably, while stones are warm. Falls of both types cool quickly, which shows that the heat was only skin deep and that the meteorites remained at their preatmospheric temperature except for a thin crustal layer. In no case has grass, hay, or other inflammable material under a freshly fallen meteorite been charred or scorched. Actually, in a few of the cases when stony meteorites have been collected immediately after falling, thin icy coats have been reported. These stones probably were central fragments of large bodies that had not come to thermal equilibrium. Reports that a meteorite was red hot or glowing when found may be discounted and attributed to preconceptions.

Number and Mass of Meteorites

According to Leonard, already some 500 tons of meteorites are in museums. From the number of meteorites that fall within the central region of the United States we estimate that the total falling over this country is 25 each year. For the whole earth the number is 2000 per year, 5 or 6 per day. From more than 400 falls the average mass collected is 20 kilograms, but a sizable portion of each meteorite must be lost as it passes through the atmosphere and by scattering of fragments over a large area. To allow for this loss, we assume that the average weight of each meteorite was 100 kilograms before it entered the atmosphere. Then the earth's total accretion of meteorites throughout a year is approximately 200 tons, about half a ton per day.

Large Meteorites

The largest known meteorite, called Hoba West and shown in Plate 36, is a roughly rectangular block weighing approximately 60 tons, 3 by 3 meters on top, with a thickness varying from 0.8 to 1 meter. It lies in limestone where it was found near Grootfontein, South West Africa. Surrounding the mass is a layer of laminated iron-shale that follows the contours of the meteorite; allowance for the metal in this shale brings the original mass to more than 80 tons. The meteorite is unusually rich in nickel, containing 16 percent, and is unusually malleable and difficult to cut. Two natives required two full days and a great quantity of hack-saw blades to cut a surface only 8 by 13 centimeters.

Second in size is Ahnighito (The Tent), Plate 37. This mass, with two others, The Woman and The Dog, were brought from Cape York, Greenland in 1897 by the explorer Peary. The three masses belong to the American Museum of Natural History in New York City, and are usually on display at the Hayden Planetarium. A fourth Cape York meteorite, Savik, is in Copenhagen. The weights of these four large masses are not well determined. Weights computed from their sizes run as high as 59 tons for Ahnighito, nearly 3 tons for The Woman, about 0.5 ton for The Dog, and 3 tons for Savik. There is evidence that as these great metallic masses lay on the ice Eskimos were slowly able to pound off fragments which they used as knives and spear tips.

The largest meteorite found in the United States and the fourth largest in the world, also on exhibition at the Hayden Planetarium in New York City, comes from near Willamette, Oregon. This conical mass of 14 tons has a number of great cavities on one side, as Plate 38 shows. These may have existed before the body met the earth or they may have been formed by rusting. The meteorite was discovered in 1902 on property belonging to the Oregon Iron and Steel Company. The discoverer, who lived nearby, spent 3 months secretly at work in the forest moving the mass to his own property. Shortly after he began to exhibit it, the Oregon Iron and Steel Company filed suit to regain possession. Eventually the Supreme Court of Oregon ruled that it belonged to the owner of the land on which it was found. In some countries meteorites belong to the government and in others it is "finders keepers."

Seven meteorites weighing a ton or more have been found in the uplands of Northern Mexico; at least one of the masses was known to the conquistadores. The largest of these bodies, Bacubirito, having an estimated mass of 24 tons, lies where it was unearthed in the state of Sinaloa. At Chupaderos in Chihuahua two masses of 14 and 6.5 tons lay 100 meters apart. Their surface features dovetail and indicate that they originally formed a single body. The fourth of these giant meteorites is Morito (El Morito), a beautiful conical mass of 20 tons. The Chupaderos masses and Morito are on display in Mexico City.

Metallic meteorites exceeding a ton have also been found in Tanganyika Territory, Africa, in Brazil, in Argentina, and in Australia. Reports of exceedingly large meteorites appear from time to time but as yet they have not been verified. A body with the fabulous length of 100 meters and height of 20 meters has been reported as near Chinguetti in the Adrar Desert, French West Africa. A small sample examined in Paris was meteoritic, but the main mass has not been visited by a scientist and upon inspection, if it can ever be found, will probably prove to be much smaller than the reported dimensions.

Meteor Craters

Each year billions of tiny, millions of small, and thousands of large bodies strike the earth. So far we have discussed only the characteristics of the small and moderate-sized bodies, but occasionally the earth encounters a huge one. For these great masses the violence of the impact is terrific. A body several hundred meters in diameter, having a mass of many million tons, will pierce the earth's atmosphere without being appreciably checked and crash into the ground while moving 15 to 70 kilometers per second. The devastation that follows is difficult to describe in detail, but some effects are self-evident in the form of meteor craters.

As the mass plunges into the ground its forward motion is checked in a minute fraction of a second. Through this braking action the outer parts of the meteorite and the ground in contact with it are tremendously compressed, heated, and partly turned to vapor. This gas, with steam from the omnipresent ground water, expands in a terrific explosion, blowing much of the meteorite back out of the ground and tearing a gaping crater. The meteorite is shattered and widely scattered over the surrounding area; at best a fraction of the original body remains in the crater. An intensely hot air blast spreads out, burning and destroying nearby plant and animal life. Simultaneously, strong earth waves spread from the crater, warping and shattering the surrounding rock strata.

At the beginning of the twentieth century the Barringers and their associates suggested that the large crater in Arizona had a meteoritic origin. Geologists were reluctant to accept this novel explanation and contended that the more familiar processes associated with volcanic action, steam blowouts, or sinks were more probable. Gradually, however, indisputable evidence supporting the meteoritic origin appeared and now this explanation is generally accepted. With the Barringer Crater in Arizona as an example, geologists are alert for similar craters that defy explanation by the common geological processes. In no case, however, is the meteoritic explanation acceptable until all the ordinary crater-forming processes have been eliminated or unmistakable meteoritic evidence is found.

In Table 25 we summarize our present knowledge of 12 meteor craters or groups of craters accepted as having meteoric origin. Similar origin has been suggested for other craters, but as yet the evidence is inconclusive. In the following pages we shall explore the salient features of these craters to see how they reveal the process of formation.

Barringer Crater, Arizona

The Barringer Meteor Crater, the first recognized, is situated between Winslow and Flagstaff, Arizona, in a large dry plateau of stratified limestone and sandstone (Plate 39). It is nearly circular and averages 1200 meters across. The rim rises 37 meters above the surrounding plain, while the present depth is 175 meters from the rim to the crater floor. Many rocks in and around the crater show mute evidence of the crushing impact. Tons of pulverized sandstone constitute a fine rock flour, both under the crater floor and around the rim. Other sandstone fragments show evidence of melting, being fused and spongy, sometimes including particles of metal. Still other fragments (Plate 40) reveal how the original horizontal bandings in the rocks were warped and twisted by the blow. To a distance of several kilometers from the crater thousands of metallic meteorites, weighing from a few grams to 500 kilograms, lay intermingled with rock fragments. Enthusiastic collectors have already removed nearly all the meteoritic material, and at present a sample can rarely be found on the surface. With electric and magnetic detecting devices sizable chunks can, however, be located and excavated from depths of 2 to 3 meters. A few more years of such gleaning will completely strip this region of meteorites. Throughout all the investigations, no meteorite of any size has been found inside the crater. Some small exposed meteorites have been completely oxidized and now constitute "shale balls," or iron-stone, while others are partly oxidized but contain metallic cores.

Table 25. Meteor craters.

Name	Number	Diameter * (meters)	Date of discovery	Meteorites
Barringer, Arizona	1	1200	1891	Metallic
Odessa, Texas	2	170	1921	Metallic
Brenham, Kansas	1	17	1933	Stony-iron
Campo del Cielo, Argentina	Many	75	—	Metallic
Henbury, Australia	13	200×110	1931	Metallic
Boxhole, Australia	1	175	1937	Metallic
Dalgaranga, Australia	1	70	1923	Metallic
Wabar, Arabia	2	100	1932	Metallic
Oesel, Estonia	6	100	1927	Metallic
Tunguska, Siberia	10 or more	50	1908–23	—
Sikhote–Alin, Siberia	106	28	1947	Metallic
Wolf Creek, Australia	1	850	1947	"Iron stone"
New Quebec, Canada	1	3,400	1950	None found

* Diameter of the largest crater when there are more than one.

During the earliest investigations the circular shape misled the Barringers into the assumption that the meteorite fell vertically. Numerous drill holes through the crater floor passed through a few hundred meters of pulverized and shattered rock containing small metallic particles and then into relatively undisturbed layers. The lack of meteoritic material under the crater and the undisturbed condition of the deep underlying strata were a great puzzle. Finally, several clues gave the correct answer. Barringer noticed that rifle bullets striking mud at a large angle make not elliptical but circular holes. Then he saw that the exposed strata in the crater rim have been tilted upward and sloped away from the center. In the northern rim this tilt is only 5°, but it steadily increases around the eastern and western walls until in the southeast and southwest the exposed strata are nearly vertical. Across the southern rim a broad arch, 800 meters long, has been raised vertically 32 meters (Plate 41). These peculiarities suggest that the meteor struck from the north at a considerable angle and penetrated under the southern rim. Once this possibility was clear, the earlier drill holes gave supporting evidence, for those through the southern part of the crater floor went deepest before encountering undisturbed rocks. A churn drill was driven down through the southern rim of the crater (Fig. 50). Below 365 meters

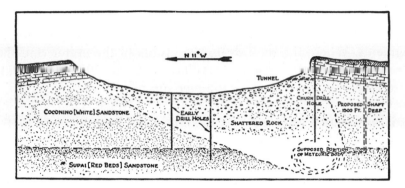

Fig. 50. Cross-section of the Barringer meteor crater. The rocks under the crater are shattered but lie much as they did before the impact of the meteor crushed them. (Reproduced by permission from the Scientific American.)

it passed through a region increasingly rich in meteoritic material and at 410 meters struck a region containing 75 percent nickel-iron which was exceedingly resistant to boring. After passing through 10 meters of this material the drill finally stuck and remains today immovable. Later electric and magnetic surveys of the region around the crater suggest that a sizable amount of metallic material lies under the southern rim, but estimates of the amount and location vary.

In the soil around this crater Nininger has discovered myriads of grains that are attracted by a magnet. Their origin is not thoroughly understood, but they may shed new light on the crater-forming process. No one knows how long ago this crater was formed. We can only estimate from the rate at which it is eroded and from the rate at which the meteorites rust away forming "shale balls" of sand grains cemented together by iron oxides. Certainly the crater had no recent origin; many estimates put the origin back 5000 years, but even 75,000 years is not an impossible interval since the day it was blasted in this arid plateau.

Other American Craters

Two other meteor craters are known in the United States. Near Odessa, in western Texas, a crater roughly 170 meters in diameter and 5 meters deep was discovered in 1921. Several small meteorites (Plate 35) and "shale balls" were found there; later Nininger dragged this region with a magnetic rake and collected 1500 metallic fragments. Where the rock strata are visible in the crater rim, they slope away from the center at angles of 20° to 30°. Sellards and Barnes have supervised magnetometer surveys which indicated that considerable iron lies 50 meters below the surface. Drill holes and partial excavation revealed that the crater has been filled 20 meters deep with silt and sand. Below this lie debris and considerable pulverized rock. A second crater 24 meters across and 7 meters deep was found and several other smaller craters were suspected. The eroded condition of the craters and the weathered state of the meteorites indicate a great age for the craters. During the excavations bones of extinct animals were found; these indicate that the craters were formed many thousands of years ago.

Near Brenham, Kansas, fragments of stony-iron meteorites were discovered in 1885, and from an area of several square kilometers nearly a ton of material was collected during the next few years. In 1933 Nininger began excavating a previously unnoticed "buffalo wallow." It proved to be a meteor crater 17 by 11 meters in area and about 3 meters deep; the long dimension lies along a line WNW to ESE. Within the crater Nininger found several meteorites weighing up to 26 kilograms and hundreds of small partly oxidized fragments. Over a kilometer away four additional masses totaling over half a ton were unearthed from depths of 30 to 60 centimeters.

At Campo del Cielo in the Gran Chaco of Argentina are a number of round shallow depressions, the largest being 75 meters across with a rim rising 1 meter above the surrounding plain. Nearby lie several iron meteorites with masses exceeding a ton. Later, one of the depressions, 53 meters in diameter and 5 meters deep, was partially excavated. Underneath were "white ash," "transparent glass," and small fragments of meteoritic iron. The "ash" and "glass" were similar to the rock flour and fused silica found at the Arizona Crater. Further investigation of these depressions should be made as soon as possible, for they may prove to be one of the world's largest groups of meteor craters.

In 1950 a prospector, Mr. F. W. Chubb, noted on aerial photographs a peculiar circular lake-filled crater (Plate 42), now known as the New Quebec Crater, among the glacial finger lakes of the Ungava Peninsula of northern Quebec. With the suspicion that this might be a great new meteorite crater, Dr. V. B. Meen led a party of geologists and explorers to the site. The crater is in a sheet of granite that shows no evidence of volcanic activity. The rim, 150 meters high, is upturned and similar to that of the Barringer Crater. The lake within the crater is 250 meters deep, but no borings have been made to determine how much deeper the undisturbed strata lie. The terrain around the crater is so strewn with granite boulders that search for possible meteorites was unsuccessful. Yet the evidence is exceedingly strong that this is the largest meteorite crater yet discovered. Figure 51 shows how it compares in size and depth with the Barringer Crater and the Wolf Creek Crater in Australia.

Australian Craters

In 1931 a group of thirteen craters and much meteoritic iron was found in central Australia, near Henbury. Alderman, who investigated the region, showed conclusively that the craters were of meteoritic origin. Twelve of the craters are roughly circular, with diameters ranging between 9 and 80 meters. The largest crater is oval, with dimensions of 200 and 110 meters, and it is 12 to 15 meters deep; apparently it was formed by the overlapping of two adjacent craters. In the smallest of the craters, the one 9 meters across, four fragments of meteoritic iron, the weathered remains of a single mass weighing 200 kilograms, were found 3 meters below the ground level. In the formation of this small crater the energy generated was not sufficient to completely shatter and eject the intruding mass.

The metal collected around the Henbury craters contains 7.3 percent of nickel and shows the crystal pattern peculiar to meteorites.

In the smallest fragments, some of which are twisted slugs, this pattern has been partially destroyed, evidence that they have been momentarily heated to at least 850°C. These craters are in a semiarid region like the plateau of Arizona and their eroded condition suggests an age comparable to that of the Barringer crater. Yet the natives fear the region and speak of it as "sun walk fire devil rock." This sounds like a cryptic description of the meteor and crater-forming explosion, which poses an interesting question for anthropologists — how long will primitive peoples transmit legends and taboos?

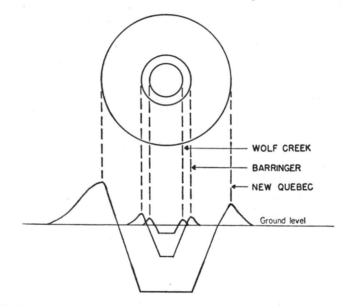

Fig. 51. Diagrammatic comparison of the New Quebec Crater, the Barringer Crater, and the Wolf Creek Crater. The vertical scale is magnified approximately 7 times over the horizontal scale. Depths shown are to the present crater floors; the New Quebec Crater is filled with a lake 250 meters deep. Modified with permission from diagram by Dr. V. B. Meen, J. Roy. Astron. Soc. Can. 44, 169 (1950).

At Boxhole, about 300 kilometers northeast of Henbury, is a crater 175 meters across and 10 to 16 meters deep, with a rim 3 to 5 meters high. This crater, found in 1937, is weatherbeaten and probably quite old. Nearby were "shale balls" and fragments of meteoritic metal and a meteorite weighing 82 kilograms. Near Dalgaranga a crater 70 meters wide and 5 meters deep was discovered in 1923. Around its rim, especially on the northwest side, sizeable rock fragments have been tilted up. In the vicinity were many fragments of meteoritic iron having a bent and confused structure like that of the small pieces found at Henbury.

Another large crater in Australia is probably meteoritic but requires detailed study. In 1947 geologists in an airplane noted the Wolf Creek crater. A brief inspection on the ground revealed that the crater is about 850 meters in diameter and its floor is perhaps 30 meters below the surrounding sandstone plain (Plate 44). A rim of shattered sandstone tilts outward from the crater and rises in places to 30 meters above the plain. The description is similar to that of the Barringer Crater. Although no meteorites were found at Wolf Creek, some iron-stone, possibly oxidized meteorites, has been collected. Sizeable trees within the crater, a nearly level floor, and other evidences of wind and water erosion indicate that the crater was formed long ago.

Arabian and Estonian Craters

Far from Australia, near Wabar in the Desert of Arabia, are two unusual meteor craters. Both are hardly more than depressions in the desert; the larger is nearly circular, with a diameter of 100 meters and a depth of 12 meters, and the smaller is 55 by 40 meters. The shifting desert sands have nearly concealed the deep pits and shattered structure in the underlying rock. Nearby were found several pieces of meteoric iron and numerous masses of frozen silica foam containing shiny metallic globules (Plate 45). Not only was the sand liquefied, but it was even vaporized, for the surfaces of the glassy chunks show dewlike drops of condensed silica. Some idea of the temperature developed in the explosion may be obtained from the geological thermometer given by Spencer: iron melts at 1535°C, silica melts at 1710°, iron boils at 2900°, silica boils at 3500°.

Far to the north, on the Baltic Sea island of Oesel, there are six craters, of which the largest is nearly circular with a diameter of 100 meters and a rim 6 meters above ground level. Rock powder and fragments appear in the rim and under the crater. Since this crater is occupied by a lake, thorough study of it is impossible, but in nearly every feature it is a miniature of the Barringer crater. Of the five other craters, four are circular, approximately 35, 33, 20, and 10 meters across. The fifth is oval, 53 by 36 meters, but deeper at one end; it probably was formed from two overlapping circular depressions. Reinwaldt, formerly with the mining industry of Estonia, extensively studied the craters after 1927 by cutting trenches across them, and completely excavated the 20-meter crater. In all cases the results were similar: the limestone strata comprising the walls have been raised and slope away from the center at angles of 30° to 40°. In the jagged edges of the upturned strata are large quantities of pulverized rock, while below lie strata in their normal horizontal position. In the rock below the center of the excavated crater Reinwaldt found a short funnel 1 meter wide and 0.5 meter deep (Plate 46). The adjacent limestone is cracked and has a burnt appearance.

After ten years of effort Reinwaldt in 1937 found conclusive proof of the meteoritic origin of these craters in the form of 28 small fragments of meteoritic iron totaling 110 grams. That large masses are not found now is not surprising, for the island has been inhabited and tilled for centuries and any sizable metallic masses were probably removed long ago.

Siberian Craters

On the morning of June 30, 1908 (at 0h 16m Greenwich Civil Time) a great meteor blazed northward over central Siberia and crashed to the earth in an isolated region near the Stony Tunguska River. The resulting explosion was so tremendous that windows were broken 80 kilometers away, and 700 kilometers away on the Trans-Siberian Railway an engineer stopped his train for fear it would be thrown off the track. For many years the rumors about this great meteor received no scientific attention, but finally in 1923 a Russian scientist, Kulik, began collecting reports. In 1927 he led an expedition to the region and near latitude 61° N, longitude 102° E found a great area of devastation centered around at least ten craters ranging from 10 to 50 meters across. Other expeditions went to the highly inaccessible region, where the ground is frozen all winter and turns to marsh with the thaws; in 1930–31 Kulik established a camp here and explored the craters for thirteen months. Under one crater he found rock flour and fused quartz containing minute grains of nickel-iron.

Around the craters the devastation was frightful. Over a small central area tree trunks stood vertically, stripped of their branches and seared by fire (Plate 47). Out to a distance of 30 kilometers all the trees had been blown over and lay along lines radiating from the craters. Even at distances of 60 to 90 kilometers the effects of the blast were apparent.

Accompanying the explosion a great pillar of smoke shot up at least 20 kilometers into the atmosphere. On the nights following the fall European observers noted especially beautiful twilights and what seemed to be very high cirrus clouds. These probably were caused by dust and smoke that spread through the upper atmosphere from the explosion. If this meteorite had met the earth just 4 hours and 47 minutes later, we should have known of the blast much sooner, for it would have scored a bull's-eye hit upon the city of St. Petersburg, now called Leningrad.

The explosion wave spread out causing deviations in the barographic records at many Siberian stations. Five hours after the impact the air wave reached England, 5500 kilometers from the fall point. Not only was an air wave observed, but European seismographs recorded a strong ground wave. From the energy liberated in these waves and in the destruction at the fall point, the mass of the meteorites is estimated as a few hundred tons, comparable to a locomotive. The destruction caused by this meteor seems tremendous, yet the craters formed are among the smallest known. These depressions in a marsh and decimated forest will disappear in a few hundred years and nothing will remain to indicate their former existence.

At 10:35 on February 12, 1947 another great meteor crashed to earth in the Soviet Union. This one, seemingly as bright as the sun, came from the north at an angle of 60° to the vertical. It hit the earth in the Sikhote-Alin Mountains at latitude 49° 10′ N and longitude 134° 39′ E a few hundred kilometers north of Vladivostok. A great brownish column of dust rose about 30 kilometers into the atmosphere.

Soviet scientists who hurried to the area found a scene reminiscent of that created by the Tunguska meteor of 1908. One hundred six craters with diameters up to 28 meters and depths of 10 meters were surrounded by trees felled radially from each of the main craters.

Other trees appeared to have been tossed high in the air and lay like jackstraws. The fall area is at least 5 kilometers long and 2 wide, with the largest craters at the southern end. Five tons of meteoritic iron, classified variously as coursest octahedrite or as hexahedrite and often twisted like the small fragments from Henbury, were collected. Probably much more escaped detection in the forest. The two largest masses found weigh 300 kilograms each, while the smallest fragments are tiny specks. Apparently a considerable portion of the original material was backfired out of the craters, which resemble Henbury, Oesel, and Brenham.

Two additional suspected meteoritic craters have been reported from the East Pamir region of Tadzhik SSR. Located just north of India, these craters are near 74° 17′ E and 38° 06′ N. In 1926 Klavins found a crater 79 meters wide and 15 meters deep. In 1951 a scientific expedition found a second crater 16 meters wide some 250 meters away. Although no meteorites have been reported, the limestone rock below these craters has been burned several millimeters deep; the structure is similar to that at Oesel. Nomads report that a fiery star fell there 200 to 300 years ago and the local name for the spot means "the place where lightning fell."

Further exploration in the dry, desert areas of the earth are likely to reveal additional meteor craters. In the Sahara Desert one crater, known as Talemzane, in Algeria shows many characteristics of the great meteor craters. It is about 1700 meters across, larger than the Barringer Crater, and the upturned rim rises 70 meters higher than the crater floor. This is strongly suggestive of a meteoritic origin, but no meteorites have been found. Elsewhere in the Sahara several smaller craters look interesting. At one, silica glass, similar to that at Wabar, has been found.

Meteor Craters in General

From the descriptions of the meteor craters or groups of craters mentioned we can see that the outstanding characteristics of such craters are: nearly circular shape; upward-tilted rims that slope away from the center; and the presence of meteoritic material nearby. If the place of impact contains sand or sandstone, chunks of frozen silica will be formed by the liquefaction and vaporization of the sand with subsequent condensation and freezing. The material surrounding and lying under the crater is always bent and warped by the force of the impact. The small excavated craters at Henbury, Brenham, and Oesel illustrate the transition between the splashed or gouged pits made by small meteorites and the large explosion craters. At Henbury four pieces of metal lay in the smallest crater. The larger Brenham Crater contained numerous fragments whose size increased with depth, but no single large mass. At Oesel the crater 20 meters across contained no meteoritic material, but a scar reveals the point at which the explosive forces were concentrated. Larger craters are all formed on the same pattern, having circular shapes and up-turned rims. The multiplicity of craters at several of the locations suggests that small swarms of metallic bodies may strike the earth together.

At present only a few widely separated and relatively inaccessible meteor craters are known; but since their reality has been recognized for only a few decades, many similar depressions doubtless await discovery. Few of these will be near cities because cities are usually built in areas of high rainfall where craters are rapidly obliterated by erosion. Furthermore, the intensive cultivation that generally surrounds cities also acts as an eraser. From the number of craters known we can estimate that several meteoritic craters 10 meters or more in diameter are blasted in the earth each century.

Fossil Craters and Lunar Craters

Fossil meteor craters, the remnants of great ancient craters, may, according to the discussions of Boon and Albritton, dot the earth. These investigators point out that during very long intervals of time erosion will remove the rocks surrounding the upper portions of a crater and expose the underlying folded and shattered strata. In the south and west of the United States are circular structures several kilometers across that exhibit bilateral symmetry, central uplifts, and extremely pulverized rocks. Although these are generally attributed to the explosion of volcanic gases, geologists find little evidence for intense volcanic activity during the era when these depressions were formed. Such a crater several kilometers across would be formed if the earth collided with one of the closely approaching asteroids. The fossil craters may be the eroded marks of such collisions in the

145

distant past. Until we know more about the deep underlying structure of large craters we shall not be certain how the fossil craters were formed.

With his customary boldness, R. A. Daly speculated on the possible meteoritic origin of the great Vredefort ring structure in South Africa. The central core of this structure, more than 30 kilometers across, is composed of Old Granite. Surrounding the core is a collar of stratified rocks tilted at high angles with radial symmetry. Geological evidence puts the age of this structure at several hundred million years, during which time extensive erosion and other processes have altered its original appearance. While many geological mechanisms have been suggested to explain this structure, meteoritic impact seems consistent with the geological and geophysical evidence and not astronomically impossible.

If great meteorites are blasting craters in the earth, they must be doing the same on the moon, which lacks any protecting atmosphere. The surface of our satellite is well pitted with yawning craters, the largest of which are 150 kilometers across, while thousands exceed the size of the Barringer Meteor Crater. Although we are sure that millions of meteors strike the moon each day, there is no conclusive proof that any observable change in lunar topography has occurred within the past century. The larger lunar features seem to most astronomers to be the scars formed when sizable solid bodies hit the moon long ago.

☆

☆ **10** ☆

Meteorites in the Laboratory

In 1803, after years of skepticism, the French Academy, representing the scientific world, officially acknowledged that stones could and did fall to the earth from surrounding space. Previously, dark stones found after "thunderstorms," some of which occurred under cloudless skies, were attributed to the action of lightning upon accumulations of dust in the atmosphere or upon ordinary rocks. At the end of the eighteenth century Chladni was convinced that meteorites originated somewhere off the earth and he was supported in this conclusion by the researches of Brandes and Benzenberg upon ordinary meteors. But it remained for Biot to make such a thorough investigation of the fall of stones at L'Aigle, France, April 26, 1803, that the skeptical academicians were convinced, and the scientific world acknowledged the existence of meteorites. An extramundane origin was, however, not immediately accepted everywhere by the general populace. Upon hearing of a stone that fell from the sky at Weston, Connecticut on December 17, 1807, Thomas Jefferson, then President of the United States, reputedly said, "I could more easily believe that two Yankee professors would lie than that stones would fall from heaven."

Here, at last, in the meteorites, we have some of the interplanetary material that we can handle, scrutinize, analyze, and test with every device in the laboratory (Plate 49). What meteorites are and how they are put together seems a matter that should have been settled long ago. But we are still far from having the complete answer. Their

147

study requires the comprehensive and coöperative work of many types of scientists — mineralogists, metallurgists, chemists, petrologists, physicists, and astronomers — each of whom has his own particular interest and line of inquiry. During the nineteenth century many capable mineralogists and chemists accumulated isolated facts about the mineralogical and chemical structure of meteorites, but could form no coherent and consistent explanation for what they observed. They needed the advice and assistance of other scientists, for the findings in each subject limit the possible explanations to be drawn from the others. In the study of meteorites many new techniques are used; microchemical analysis, crystal examination with x-rays, isotope studies with mass spectographs, and the study of nuclear transformations offer the possibility of gaining the fundamental information necessary for new attempts to account for these strange and complex bodies.

The colors and reflectivities of meteorites compared to asteroids might provide definite evidence as to whether these bodies have similar chemical compositions. Color measurements of 50 stony meteorites showed that all but one reddened light slightly upon reflection, much as do the asteroids. The reflectivities of these stony meteorites ranged from 5 percent, a very dark gray surface, to 50 percent, a whitish surface; the asteroids listed in Table 6 have a similar range of reflectivities. Furthermore, the few metallic meteorites studied have colors and reflectivities like those of stony meteorites. Although both stony and metallic meteorites reflect light like the asteroids, most plutonic rocks on the earth also treat light similarly. Consequently, this line of study has not provided clear-cut evidence about the similarity of meteorites and asteroids.

Chemical Composition

In his laboratory the chemist can soon determine which chemical elements are abundant in meteorites and in what quantities. But when he begins searching for minute traces of some elements, his troubles increase rapidly. Thus it was long rumored that gold and silver existed in meteorites, but the precious metals were found in the metallic meteorites only through painstaking work, for their total quantity averages but 60 grams in a ton. Measurement of the radioactive elements — radium, uranium, and thorium — was even more difficult. In the metallic meteorites the total uranium and thorium runs less than 0.1 gram to the ton, but in the stony meteorites they are about six times as abundant. For comparison we note that the average ton of granite contains 20 grams of the radioactive elements.

Taking many meteorites we find the average compositions given in Table 26. Compared with the earth's crust, the stony meteorites are deficient in oxygen and silicon, so we cannot expect to find the same compounds and minerals in meteorites as in the average terrestrial rock.

Table 26. Composition of meteorites and of the earth's crust (percent).

Element	Meteorites		Earth's crust
	Irons	Stones	
Oxygen		36.3	49.4
Iron	90.8	24.1	4.7
Silicon		18.0	25.8
Magnesium		13.9	1.9
Sulfur	0.04	1.8	0.05
Calcium		1.7	3.4
Aluminum		1.5	7.5
Nickel	8.5	1.5	0.02
Sodium		0.7	2.6
Chromium	0.01	.30	0.03
Manganese		.26	.08
Potassium		.18	2.4
Phosphorus	.17	.14	0.12
Cobalt	.59	.14	
Carbon	.03		.09
Copper	.02		.01

But averages such as those in Table 26 mask the diversity that we find in various individual meteorites (Plate 50). In metallic meteorites the nickel content varies from 5 to over 20 percent. Fortunately, none of the terrestrial nickel-iron alloys have nickel contents within this range, so the quantity of nickel in a piece of nickel-iron is a good test of whether or not it is a meteorite. The silica content of meteoric stones varies between 30 and 55 percent and produces a corresponding diversity in their mineralogical structure. Table 27 shows other variations in their chemical composition. Some of the irregularities

149

are interrelated; for example, the abundance of magnesium varies inversely with that of calcium and aluminum. In Chapter 6 we have already seen how the varying abundances of calcium and magnesium may affect the spectra of fireballs.

We may ask the chemist to derive an average composition for all meteorites, but he declines and points out that the average composition depends upon the relative quantity of stone and metal that fall. This is a problem for the astronomer and the meteorite collector. Stony falls usually consist of many fragments scattered over a wide

Table 27. *Variations in abundance of some metallic oxides in stony meteorites.*

Oxide	Abundance (percent)		
	Maximum	Minimum	Average
Al_2O_3	13.50	0.10	2.86
MgO	35.80	7.14	23.66
CaO	24.51	0.00	1.88
Na_2O	3.96	0.00	0.87
Fe + FeO	33.95	1.74	25.95

area. If one piece is seen to fall, a search reveals other pieces that increase the total recorded weight. In contrast, the tougher irons rarely split; usually either what seems to be the whole mass is collected or nothing is found. Through disruption and the wide scattering of fragments the number of stony meteorites seen to fall is disproportionally increased, but through this same scattering many fragments are lost; as a result the quantity of stony material collected per fall is much less than the quantity actually reaching the ground. We find that 392 stony falls weigh 7705 kilograms while 21 iron falls weigh 730 kilograms. Thus, although the total weight of these stony falls is ten times that of the irons, the average iron fall weighs nearly twice is much as does the average stone. These uncertainties prohibit an exact statement of the proportions of falling stone and iron, but suggest that the stony material is from four to nine times as abundant as the metallic. Table 28 includes the average composition computed for these proportions. Harrison Brown concluded, from analogy with the earth, that the ratio of silicate to metal is near 3/2; but such an analogy has its dangers.

In calculating this table we have assumed that our museums contain a true sample of the various materials striking the atmosphere. But we may be mistaken. At least one copper mass believed to be a meteorite has been found. We have, moreover, little chance of finding any "icy" bodies like those that might compose a comet, if any should penetrate the atmosphere.

Meteorites contain various gases. When investigators in the nineteenth century pulverized and heated metallic meteorites they obtained considerable quantities of hydrogen (H_2) and carbon monoxide (CO), with lesser percentages of carbon dioxide (CO_2) and

Table 28. *Mean composition (percent) of meteorites, assuming different ratios by weight of stones to irons.*

Element	Ratio by weight of stones to irons	
	4	9
Carbon	0.14	0.15
Oxygen	29.00	32.70
Sodium	0.24	0.27
Magnesium	11.00	12.88
Aluminum	0.61	0.68
Silicon	14.40	16.28
Phosphorus	0.11	0.10
Sulfur	1.90	1.87
Chlorine	0.02	0.03
Potassium	.06	.06
Calcium	1.10	1.18
Titanium	0.08	0.09
Chromium	.12	.12
Manganese	.15	.16
Iron	38.00	31.85
Cobalt	0.22	0.18
Nickel	2.80	2.08
Copper	0.02	0.01

nitrogen (N_2). Methane (CH_4) was reported from two meteorites. Stony meteorites gave mostly carbon dioxide with some hydrogen and traces of carbon monoxide and methane. Since these are the gases observed in comets, identification of meteorites as the solid material in comets was suggested. But extraction of the gases by heating is now known to result in chemical compounds, especially those involving carbon, not at all representative of the gases actually within metallic material. Nash has obtained gases from six metallic meteorites by carefully dissolving them without heating in gas-free solvents. He found, using current laboratory techniques, only about 1 percent of the quantities of gas reported earlier from metallic meteorites. Carbon monoxide is the most prevalent gas. Hydrogen and carbon dioxide are present, while nitrogen is less abundant. No traces of methane or of cyanogen could be found. The relatively uniform abundances of hydrogen and nitrogen (essentially equal to those obtained from steels) suggests that these meteorites originated from a common primeval mass.

Since meteorites come from outside the earth, they might have originated where the chemical elements differed from those at hand. We ask the physicist to check this by examining the abundances of isotopes — atoms having identical chemical properties but different weights. In many terrestrial materials the relative abundance of isotopes has been found to be constant. At least nine elements — carbon, oxygen, silicon, chlorine, iron, nickel, cobalt, gallium, and sulfur — from meteorites have been tested. In no case did their isotopic abundances differ significantly from those of terrestrial materials. Studies of nuclear reactions indicate that, with only a few exceptions, the relative abundances of various isotopes should be essentially constant throughout the observable universe.

Chemical Compounds

We can learn much about the origin of meteorites by noting how the atoms are joined together as compounds. Investigations with x-rays show that in the metallic alloy the nickel and iron do not form a chemical compound, for their atoms are not arranged with the required regularity. Included within the nickel-iron are, however, a number of compounds. The most abundant is iron sulfide, called troilite, which appears in a variety of shapes, most frequently as rough spheroids or as bands. Phosphorus occurs in a complex compound with iron, nickel, and cobalt called schreibersite, found only in meteorites. Schreibersite is brittle, white, and strongly magnetic, and it occurs in several forms, most frequently as needles or plates (Plate 51). Carbon is combined with the metallic atoms as cohenite; it also occurs free in both the amorphous form — large graphite nodules in the irons of coarsest structure — and the crystalline form, as microscopic diamonds. Although their commercial value is nil and they enhance the difficulties of properly polishing the materials in which they occur, the presence of diamonds is an important clue to the past history of meteorites because, although the origin of natural diamonds is not clearly understood, high temperatures and pressures were involved in their formation. One compound seldom present in any quantity, but often present in traces, is a metallic chloride, lawrencite, which hastens the rusting and decomposition of meteorites. The great 3-ton Cranbourne meteorite from Australia was rusting so rapidly that it had to be placed in a special nitrogen-filled case.

The chemical compounds found in stony meteorites are chiefly complex silicates similar to those in igneous rocks. For all silicates the fundamental unit is the tetrahedron of four oxygen atoms around a single silicon atom. In this compact group the silicon atom fits snugly into the central space, which accounts for the chemical and physical stability of the silicates, as, for example, their low solubility and high melting points. These tetrahedrons may join in various ways to produce numerous minerals: as plates to form mica, in chains to form asbestos, or in networks of varying tightness. In each of the various silicate families the number of atoms is constant; the pyroxenes contain 10 atoms and the feldspars 13. Aluminum atoms occasionally replace some but apparently never more than half of the silicon atoms. When aluminum, which has three valence charges, does replace silicon, which has four, other atomic changes must also occur to keep the molecule electrically neutral while preserving the number of atoms. Thus between the related feldspars albite, $KAlSi_3O_8$, and anorthite, $CaAl_2Si_2O_8$, the replacement of one silicon atom by aluminum involves the replacement of monovalent potassium by bivalent calcium. Many changes of this type are possible within each of the silicate families and result in a hugh variety of silicate minerals.

The most common mineral in stony meteorites is the magnesium-iron silicate, olivine $(Mg, Fe)_2SiO_4$ (the notation $(Mg,Fe)_2$ means that the two atoms may be magnesium or iron in various proportions). This molecule of seven tightly packed atoms forms a dense mineral. Second in abundance are the orthorhombic pyroxenes, $(Mg, Fe)_2Si_2O_6$; three forms are generally recognized: magnesium-rich enstatite of a light hue; bronzite of intermediate hue and magnesium

153

content; and dark, iron-rich hypersthene. Monoclinic pyroxenes appear generally as minor constituents, in the form of augite, $Ca(Mg, Fe, Al)(Al, Si)_2O_6$. Feldspars, which compose 60 percent of igneous rocks, are generally found in the form of anorthite, $CaAl_2Si_2O_8$. Other compounds occasionally found include a calcium sulfide compound called oldhamite, not found terrestrially, troilite, and lawrencite. Conspicuously lacking are water, quartz, mica, and hornblende, which are constituents of the earth's crust.

Internal Structure of the Irons

After finding what the chemist can tell us about meteorites, we take them to the metallurgist, who has a variety of tools and tests to use on them. When metallic meteorites are cut, polished, and etched with dilute acid, a pattern of intersecting bands, called the Widmanstätten figure, usually appears. It consists of three portions: wide bands or lamellae of nickel-poor kamacite, narrow bounding bands of shiny nickel-rich taenite, and the areas between lamellae filled with plessite, a mixture of kamacite and taenite. These can be seen in Plate 52. The lamellae parallel the faces of an octahedron; hence the meteorites in which they appear are called octahedrites and are subdivided according to the width of the kamacite lamellae. O. C. Farrington found that as the kamacite lamellae became narrower the average nickel content increased. This is, however, at best a statistical relation, from which individual irons appear to deviate considerably; compare Hill City, Plate 49, with Grants, Plate 51. According to Henderson their nickel contents are respectively 9.21 and 9.35 percent.

Some meteorites do not show the Widmanstätten figure; those containing less than 6 or more than 12 percent of nickel have no extensive pattern and are termed respectively the nickel-poor and the nickel-rich ataxites. Among the nickel-poor ataxites are a subgroup which upon etching show fine Neumann lines, like scratches (Plate 53). These meteorites are known as the hexahedrites.

Any alloy showing a pattern like the Widmanstätten figures must consist of two crystal phases or types of metal, in this case kamacite and taenite. Each phase consists of minute grains or blocks of a few thousand atoms arranged according to a definite pattern. But no over-all pattern would appear upon the meteorite when etched unless similar grains were lined up over several centimeters. The metallurgist tells us that the directions in which the lamellae run mark the faces of a former crystal that existed when the material had a temperature near 1000°C. Since the Widmanstätten pattern often extends unbroken for 10 centimeters or more, these high-temperature crystals must have been very large. But large crystals grow slowly, especially in this metal, so we conclude that during a long interval, at least thousands of years, the atoms of the metal were slowly linking arms and lining up to form the large crystals. A few meteorites originally consisted of more than one crystal, for the large slice shown in Plate 54 exhibits six different patterns, each the vestige of a former crystal.

Metallurgists probing by means of their furnaces, microscopes, and x-rays study how the atoms of alloys behave and form new phases as their temperatures change. Our limited knowledge about nickel-iron is summarized in Fig. 52. In view of the great size of the crystals that existed in meteorites, it is surprising to find that nickel-iron is an alloy extremely difficult to study in the laboratory. As a result, our knowledge of how the nickel and iron atoms behave under various circumstances is still not complete, but the general picture seems clear. As a liquid mixture of nickel and iron cools and solidifies at 1500°C, the atoms form little grains or minute crystals. Because these show some propensity to line up parallel to one another, they gradually build up large crystals. As the temperature falls, the high-temperature grains begin to break up and form two new types of phases. One of these contains little nickel; if excess nickel is present, it is forced from this material to form a second phase rich in nickel. We identify the two types of grains with the kamacite, containing 6 percent of nickel, and the taenite, containing about 40 percent. Since they have different solubilities in acid, their locations are revealed by etching. X-rays show that nickel-poor ataxites and hexahedrites containing less than 6 percent of nickel consist only of kamacite, while the nickel-rich ataxites (Plate 55) contain considerable kamacite, but not enough to form lamellae.

This separation, or phase change, takes place within the solid material; the new grains aline themselves parallel to the grains of the high-temperature crystal and preserve its original pattern, much as

155

a piece of petrified wood retains the tree-ring pattern. We can easily destroy the Widmanstätten figure by roasting the metal at a temperature of 800°C; upon cooling only a granular structure remains. Widmanstätten patterns have been produced in metal with a composition like that of meteorites, but on a very small scale.

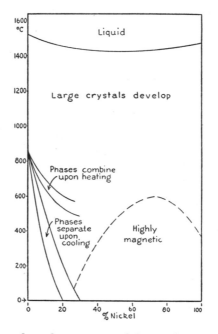

Fig. 52. *Approximate phase diagram for nickel-iron, showing how nickel-iron alloys of various compositions behave as their temperatures are changed. After solidifying from a liquid, the nickel and iron tend to separate into two types of material, one low in nickel and the other rich in nickel.*

The high degree of organization present within metallic meteorites, where the nickel-iron crystals are oriented over large areas and even the inclusions of troilite, schreibersite, and cohenite have definite forms, can only mean that this material was once liquid. Subsequently it cooled at a very slow rate, presumably while insulated deep within some large body. The time required for the formation, under high pressure, of such large crystal structures is probably quite long, perhaps a million years.

The crystal development we have suggested is probably correct, but we must remember that the pattern is never perfect, irregularities are frequent, and, according to the x-ray analysis, the individual grains are sometimes out of alinement. Furthermore, we have used pure nickel-iron for comparison, whereas meteorites contain sulfur, phosphorus, and carbon, which may influence the behavior of the nickel-iron as it cools. Yet the greater part of these impurities has been expelled from the nickel-iron to form separate crystals or nodules of cohenite, schreibersite, and troilite, as though the structure of the nickel-iron developed independently. Similar chemical separations are common in rocks such as granite, which consists of three distinct minerals.

Moreover, the recent environment of the meteorites may have had some influence on their structure. For centuries they have been separately moving through space, attaining temperatures as low as that of liquid air when they are as far from the sun as Jupiter and then warming to near room temperatures at their perihelia. There have been suggestions that the Widmanstätten figures developed as the result of intermittent heating to 550°C. To attain this temperature a meteorite must, as Fig. 3 shows, pass the sun at scarcely more than 0.1 A.U. At each such perihelion passage it would, as Fig. 4 shows, maintain such a temperature for at most a few days. Undoubtedly at one time or another some meteorites have moved this near the sun, but the Widmanstätten figure occurs in every block of metal having the proper chemical composition, whether in a large metallic meteorite or in a stony-iron. We must doubt whether the Widmanstätten pattern and the other complex structures developed through recurrent heating.

Internal Structure of Stones

The stony meteorites present an extremely complex structure, difficult to interpret. Under the microscope they show such a hodgepodge of fragmental and discolored crystals that the mineralogist has great trouble in identifying even the most common. Usually intermingled with the silicate material are numerous small inclusions of metal, troilite, and some lawrencite which oxidizes, discoloring small roundish inclusions of olivine and pyroxenes called chondrules.

The classification of stony meteorites is principally chemical, although it is also associated with their mineralogic structure. There are a few stones that have structures similar to terrestrial basalts; these stones, called achondrites, contain about 50 percent of silica, few metallic particles, and no chondrules. Plates 56 and 57 show sections of typical achondrites. Their content of radioactive material averages nearly twice that of the other stony meteorites.

The stones including chondrules, like that pictured in Plate 58, show a great variety of structure. They are principally fragments of olivine and pyroxenes, including various amounts of free metal and scattered chondrules, and range from bodies that are easily broken to fairly tough crystalline masses similar to ordinary rocks. In these latter the chondrules blend into the surrounding material of olivine and pyroxene and can barely be seen. There are also two types of dark stones, the black chondrites and the carbonaceous meteorites. The black chondrites have typical chemical compositions and internal structures, and have probably turned black as the result of being heated. The carbonaceous stones contain little metal but include many small particles of graphite widely scattered through the material. Although composing only a few percent of the total mass, this carbon gives these stones a black appearance.

Many stony meteorites appear to be composed of several types of material mixed together. One of the most obvious examples is the stone that fell at Cumberland Falls, Kentucky in 1919 (Plate 54). Here we distinctly see angular black masses embedded in whitish material of quite different composition. These mixed meteorites and the general fragmental condition of nearly all the stones are extremely difficult to explain.

If we knew how chondrules were formed and how they came to their present positions, we should be much nearer knowing how meteorites originated. The alternatives seem few; either the chondrules formed where we find them or they are inclusions. The principal difficulty with having them formed where they are found comes in explaining how they took on their shapes and internal structure while immersed in masses of splintered crystals. If we suppose that the crystals were broken after the chondrules were formed, we must explain how much of the material was shattered yet the chondrules remained intact. G. P. Merrill, of the U. S. National Museum, thought the chondrules were inclusions. He classified them into two groups:

oval pseudochondrules having a homogeneous internal structure, and the true spherical chondrules having a complex internal crystal structure. The former he thought were just pieces of olivine or pyroxene that were shaped by grinding, like the round pebbles in a stream bed. The spherical chondrules he considered as solidified droplets. Just how, when, or where these droplets formed he did not specify, nor should he be expected to, because this is a problem for the astronomer.

Strangely the crystal structures of chondrules do not radiate from their centers, as might be expected, but from eccentric points usually outside the whole chondrule. Additional studies seem only to raise more questions.

Nearly all stony meteorites include quantities of nickel-iron in the form of veins, flakes, and grains; sometimes the metal encases a silicate crystal or a chondrule. This metal contains an average of 9 percent of nickel and is entirely comparable to that comprising the largest metallic meteorites. Even its content of the precious metals is the same as that of the great metallic meteorites weighing tons. In no stone has a piece of metal been found that is large enough to show Widmanstätten figures, but x-ray analysis reveals that the atomic arrangement of this metal is identical with that of irons. How it came to be finely divided and nearly uniformly dispersed through the majority of stony meteorites is most perplexing. One authority suggested that it was produced where found through the disintegration of iron chloride, lawrencite, and that the chlorine escaped, but there is no evidence that the necessary quantities of lawrencite were ever present. Furthermore, this origin would not account for its content of the precious metals. Possibly the metal permeated the silicate in the liquid or gaseous state; but the fragmental, angular silicates show little evidence of having been heated. Some generic relation between the metal and the surrounding silicate is indicated by Prior's observation that when the metal is abundant it is rich in iron and the silicate rich in magnesium, while as the quantity of metal decreases it becomes richer in nickel and the silicate richer in iron. Yet the fragmental, mixed structure of the silicates hardly suggests that the metal quietly separated from the silicates.

Tectites

Small glassy particles called tectites (Plate 60), found in many regions of the earth, may be a type of stony meteorite that we have not previously recognized. They were first found in Bohemia, but have been turning up in many parts of the world. The regions of the East Indies and Australia contain a great supply, some have been found along the Ivory Coast of Africa, while a few have been discovered in South America and some in Texas. They are a real glass, some 77 percent silica, and in general chemical composition do not remotely resemble any known volcanic glass or terrestrial rock. They contain many small bubbles and flow marks, as though they had solidified from a liquid. As Plate 60 shows, many of them are shaped like the figure eight or like round buttons; both forms suggest that they solidified while spinning. None have been observed to fall. A meteoritic origin was suggested long ago by Suess, but only recently has the evidence supporting such a theory become at all convincing. Whatever they are, they deserve closer attention and careful study. If they are meteorites, we have one more peculiar type to add to the several already unexplained.

Stony-Irons

A small number of meteorites consisting of approximately equal parts stony and metallic materials are called stony-irons. Two types are most frequent: pallasites, in which the metal forms a continual mesh (Plate 61), and mesosiderites, in which the metal is probably discontinuous (Plate 62). Wherever sufficiently large surfaces of metal are exposed the Widmanstätten figure appears, as illustrated by Plates 61 and 62. Evidently, whatever process was responsible for this pattern in the irons has operated upon the stony-irons as well. In the pallasites the silicates are principally dense olivine, while in the mesosiderites they are olivine, pyroxenes, and feldspars. The stony-irons range from merely metal and olivine to those having a chondritic structure, and form a definite, but little populated, connecting link between the irons and the stones. Although the metal and the stone are thoroughly intermixed, each completely preserves its normal characteristics.

History of Stones

Two theories attempt to explain at least some of the peculiarities of stony meteorites. The first, more direct, hypothesis forms them by the crystallization of a molten magma but fails to account for their fragmental structure. The presence of chondrules and of metallic inclusions does not fit into such a simple explanation. The second suggestion involves a complicated multiplicity of processes. Material differing considerably in composition and structure must be pulverized, then mixed, chondrules included, and the whole compressed into a solid. Yet the orderly variation of structure, composition, and metallic content are strongly against such a mixing having occurred. Furthermore, the queries of how, when, and where such processes took place can be answered only by pyramiding postulates. As neither hypothesis satisfactorily accounts for the observed structure of the stones, we have no answer to how they formed. The principal difficulties to a satisfactory answer will be removed when the origins of chondrules and of the free metal and their relations, if any, to the adjacent silicates are better understood.

Since meteorites are continually swinging around the sun, some may venture so near that they are intensely heated. We have already noted that 3 percent of the stones, apparently typical in composition and structure, have turned black. If this results from heating, we should be able to produce similar changes in the laboratory, and when typical stones are heated to 800°C for a few minutes they do turn black. Although we are not certain that this laboratory blackening comes from the same reaction that blackened those seen to fall, the similarity of appearance is highly suggestive. If the black chondrites are ordinary stones transformed by heating, the heating might have occured when they wandered close to some star. We know the immense distances between stars and can easily calculate that any particular meteorite might wander near enough to be baked once in a million million million years. Since meteorites are less than a few thousand million years old, the chances that we would have run into one that had been heated are very small, yet we find that three in every hundred are black, so heating during interstellar wanderings is ruled out. If the sun caused the transformation, the low frequency of alteration must be explained. This is not difficult when we note that the high temperatures necessary for the transformation occur only within 0.1 A.U. of the sun and the great majority of meteorites when they met the earth were moving in orbits with perihelia outside the orbit of Venus. During their past history perturbations may have shuffled their orbits, bringing a fraction close to the sun where the heating occurred.

The Ages of Meteorites

Geochemists attempt to estimate "ages" of meteorites and many rocks by carefully measuring their contents of radium and helium. The timekeeper is the disintegration of uranium and thorium. In 4510 million years one-half of all the uranium atoms and in 13,900 million years one-half of all the thorium atoms in the universe explode. Once started on violent careers the atoms progress through a number of forms — radium constitutes one stage in the history of uranium atoms — until finally inert lead is the end product. During their disintegration the atoms shoot off electrons, gamma-rays and alpha-particles, which become helium atoms. Eight helium atoms are produced from each uranium atom and six from each thorium. When we know the rate of helium production and the amounts of helium, uranium, and thorium in a specimen, the interval required for the accumulation of this helium, or an "age," can be derived.

In meteorites the quantities of radioactive elements are exceedingly small, much less than in the average rock of the earth. Delicate electrical tests just reveal these elements in the meteorites and the measurements of their abundance is an outstanding accomplishment of modern physical chemistry. F. Paneth and his associates, who made many measurements, proceeded originally on the assumption that little thorium was present in the meteorites and, since it decayed more slowly than uranium, it would contribute at most only 10 percent of the helium atoms found in metallic meteorites which entrap the helium atoms. Later and even more careful measurements show that thorium was more abundant than previously supposed. The best measurements obtained up to 1942 appear in Table 29. The spread in the "ages" derived from them is disconcerting, for they range from 60 million years, the geologic yesterday, to 7600 million years, seemingly older than the earth. The two specimens of the Bethany meteorites have entirely different "ages" and presumably must be from entirely different falls. Paneth's earlier data showed that among the four Cape York meteorites two have unmeasurably low helium contents and appear to have "ages" less than a million years, while the other two seem to be several hundred million years old. These results were interpreted in two ways: either meteorites solidified at quite different times extending down to the geologic present, or helium leaked out of some metallic meteorites despite laboratory evidence that such leakage is inconsequential.

Table 29. Uranium-thorium-helium "ages" of metallic meteorites (Paneth, 1942).

Meteorite	Content *				Age (10⁶ yr)
	Ni	U	Th	He	
Bethany, Goamus	8	1	4	0.15	60
San Martin	5.3	0.6	8	1.6	500
Bethany, Amalia	8	1	4	3.0	1100
Carthage	7.7	0.5	4	25	6500
Thunda	8.5	.8	4	28	6100
Mount Ayliff	6.6	.4	2	40	7600

* Ni, percent; U and Th, 10^{-8} gm per gram; He, 10^{-6} cm^3 per gram.

This whole area of study was thrown into further confusion by the arguments advanced around 1948 by Bauer and by Huntley. They pointed out that high-energy cosmic rays, like atomic particles fired from cyclotrons, cause nuclear changes in iron atoms with the frequent release of alpha-particles, which become helium atoms. At the top of the earth's atmosphere and, so far as we know, between the planets, cosmic rays are far more intense than at the earth's protected surface. In interplanetary space meteorites will be bombarded by cosmic rays and accumulate helium from the induced radioactivity. This means that all the metallic meteorites may be contaminated by helium from cosmic rays and that the original "ages" derived on the assumption that all the helium was from uranium and thorium are spuriously high.

Of the helium produced by cosmic rays a sizable fraction, estimated by Le Couteur and by Singer as around 30 percent, will be the isotope helium-3. With a special mass spectrograph the ratio of helium-3 to helium-4 has been measured in a number of meteorites, as reported in Table 30. The highest ratio found was 31.5 percent in Mount Ayliff, which also has the highest total abundance of helium. After the helium-3 and attendant helium-4 attributable to cosmic rays have been subtracted, any additional helium should be of radiogenic origin, that is, arising from the disintegration of uranium and thorium. Seven meteorites of moderate helium content, for which the separation of the two types of helium is most accurate, have maximum radiogenic "ages" less than 250 million years. This is the apparent interval since they solidified.

Table 30. *Abundance and isotopic composition of helium in metallic meteorites.*

Meteorite	Helium content $(10^{-6}$ cm^3 per gram$)$	He–3/He–4 (percent)
Mount Ayliff	36.8	31.5
Carbo	22.0	28.6
Toluca (Durham)	18.9	29.7
Bethany Amalia (Krantz)	3.4	27.8
Bethany (Harvard)	0.36	17.8

The accumulation of "cosmic-ray helium" adds another means of estimating an "age" for a meteorite — the interval since the mass became a small separate body. Such cosmic-ray helium will be formed most abundantly within the outer 30 centimeters of the body. When the body plunges through the atmosphere, part of this outer material will be lost, but the observed abundance of helium-3 indicates that such loss is only moderate. Although the rate at which cosmic rays will produce helium in these meteorites has been derived only approximately, several meteorites appear to have been small solid masses exposed to cosmic rays for at least 300 million years. Yet the seven meteorites mentioned in the preceding paragraph have "cosmic-ray ages" less than 20 million years.

Equally interesting have been Paneth's repeated tests on the large Cape York irons Savik and Ahnighito and one of the Muonionalusta masses, in which no helium has been found. Yet their contents of uranium and thorium are comparable to those of other metallic meteorites. Apparently their maximum "ages," both as solid bodies and as small masses exposed to cosmic rays, cannot exceed 1 million years. Among the various meteorites we seem to have a real range in

164

both the "ages": the radiogenic age, since solidification, and the cosmic-ray age, since exposure as a small body.

While there seems to be no way of avoiding the conclusion that a real range exists in the intervals since the masses solidified and since they became exposed to cosmic rays, the discrepancies between the two types of helium ages remind us that many assumptions are involved in the age derivations. The cosmic-ray ages involve the assumption that over some millions of years the meteorites have been exposed to essentially the cosmic-ray intensity existing now outside the earth's atmosphere. Furthermore, both derivations of helium ages involve the assumption that a fair fraction of the helium has not leaked out over these long time intervals. Although laboratory experiments, necessarily of short duration, indicate that even at temperatures high enough to destroy the Widmanstätten pattern helium leakage would be slow, we can hardly assume that there has been no significant leakage during millions of years. Another suggestion has the radiogenic helium leaking out selectively in comparison with the cosmic-ray helium. At first this seems highly improbable. There is, however, some evidence that most of the cosmic-ray helium would be formed deep within the metallic crystals, while the radioactive materials and radiogenic helium may be concentrated near the crystal faces, which might allow the helium to escape more readily. Only further studies will clarify these apparent inconsistencies.

Several stony meteorites have also been examined for helium content. Despite the probable leakage of helium along cracks, the stones Pultusk and Waconda and the silicate phase of the stony-irons Brenham and Mincy contain enough helium to indicate "ages" of several hundred million years. The Beddgelert stone, which fell in North Wales in 1949, is a very hard chondrite which easily scratches glass. Within a few days after its fall Paneth tested both its silicate and its metallic phases for helium and radioactive content. While only preliminary "ages" could be given, the silicate phase seemed to have solidified more than 1000 million years ago and the metallic phase about 200 million years ago. Further studies of this type may prove especially interesting on a large stony-iron, for several lines of evidence suggest that the metallic phases did form considerably later than the silicates.

In the Soviet Union, Gerling and Pavlova have made use of the fact that potassium-40 is radioactive and becomes the chemically inert gas argon-40. For two stones they obtained "ages" of 3000 million years. Similarly, in the United States Wasserberg derived argon-potassium "ages" for two stones. His results were close to 4600 million years. These argon "intervals since solidification" greatly exceed the helium ages.

As often happens, additional information has complicated our earlier derivation of "ages." At least three different "ages," each subject to experimental difficulties and different assumptions, must now be recognized: (1) the interval during which the meteorite as a small solid body has been exposed to cosmic rays; (2) the interval during which radiogenic helium or argon has accumulated within a solid body, not necessarily small; and (3) the interval during which radiogenic lead has accumulated within a solid body, irrespective of size.

These several intervals, or "ages," focus attention upon the peculiar histories of the individual meteorites which may have solidified at different times within different bodies and become exposed to cosmic rays at different times. Some of the apparent confusion and contradictions may be reduced when the various measurements are all made upon the same, or very similar, samples from a particular chunk of meteorite.

Origin of Meteorites

Having surveyed the composition and structure of meteorites, we may speculate on how they came into existence. Our astronomical knowledge proves their extraterrestrial origin and strongly suggests that they have been permanent members of the solar system. Chemically the two types of material, stony and metallic, show minor variations, but each forms a continuous sequence from the highly chondritic stones rich in metal to the metal-free achondrites, and from the nickel-poor to the nickel-rich ataxites. Between the stones and irons certain chemical distinctions are almost complete, for example, the concentration of the precious metals in the nickel-iron and the radioactive elements in the silicate. Yet the distinct metallic and silicate phases are connected by the existence of the stony-irons and the similarity of the free metal in all types of meteorites. All this evidence indicates that the stony and the metallic meteorites form a single continuous sequence of material that must have had a common type of origin.

Some writers have attributed the origin of meteorites to the accumulation of individual interplanetary dust particles and gas atoms. While such a process might initially provide the body or bodies from which meteorites later came, we need only recall the complex chemical and physical structure of meteorites to realize that they were not built up in their present form as separate bodies by the accumulation of individual particles.

The fragmental structure of stony meteorites might be explained by the aggregation of solid particles. Yet, unless we make some weird guess about the distribution of material in space, the orderly array of chemical and mineral structure among both stones and irons is strongly against any such origin. Such theories completely neglect the continuity of structure between stones and irons. Moreover, the segregation and crystal structure of certain compounds, troilite, schreibersite, and cohenite, which sometimes are neatly encased in kamacite (Plate 62), conflicts with the origin of the irons through the accumulation of atoms or particles. The existing structures could have developed only upon slow cooling from a liquid.

This chemical and mineralogical homogeneity and continuity demand an origin for all meteorites under essentially similar conditions. Apparently they developed their present structures within one or more slowly cooling masses of near planetary size.

Analogies between meteorites and the deep structure of the earth are readily named, but we must consider them carefully, noting the discordant as well as the favorable facts. At the center of the earth is a large core extending more than halfway to the surface and having a density 11 or 12 times that of water. If relieved of the compression of the overlying materials, this core would have a density near 8, comparable to that of metallic meteorites.

Surrounding the earth's core are very basic silicates, probably similar in composition to stony meteorites. How and why the silicate and metallic materials of meteorites or of the earth would separate has been studied extensively by V. M. Goldschmidt and others. They concluded that in a great molten mixture having the composition of the earth, the silicates would separate from the metal and float to the top like slag on molten iron. The atoms of the precious metals, having nearly the same size as the atoms of nickel and iron, would be trapped in the metal. As the silicate material cooled, the dense minerals olivine and pyroxene, having the highest melting points, would solidify first and lie adjacent to the metal. As the process of separation continued, the final slag constituting the outer crust would be rich in silica, forming granite, and have a high concentration of the radioactive elements, as we find in the earth's crust. Any layer intermediate between the metallic core and the silicates would presumably consist of intermixed metal and silicates.

Such a sequence of material is represented by the nickel-iron masses; the stony-irons, varying from the pallasites, rich in metal and olivine, through the mesosiderites with less metal and more acidic silicates; and the various classes of stones with decreasing metal and increasing silica content. This sequence of meteorites is too complete to be accidental and must be attributed to a process of separation like that which brings the cream to the top of the milk bottle.

Harrison Brown and his co-workers have investigated the equilibrium relations between the abundances of various chemical compounds in meteorites and concluded that high temperatures and pressures would account for the observed relation. They tentatively suggested that the temperature was about 3000°C and the pressure about a million atmospheres, comparable to conditions deep within the earth. A body similar to the earth in size and structure seemed reasonable to Brown. However, the evidence for Table 28 hints that stony meteorites may be relatively more abundant than would result from shattering the earth. One or more smaller planets intermediate in size between the earth and Mars seem equally reasonable.

Further careful investigation of trace elements supports this parallel with a planetary structure. Pinson has found that the ratios of the abundances of potassium and rubidium and of other pairs of trace elements are constant both in stony meteorites and in many terrestrial rocks. Although these elements are most abundant in rocks of low melting point and are scarce in stony meteorites, the constancy of their relative abundances strongly suggests that the past history of stony meteorites has been similar to that of terrestrial rocks.

The equally important metallurgical evidence suggests that the irons cooled at an exceedingly low rate, which allowed their large crystal structure to develop. At the center of a cooling mass this is exactly what we might expect to happen. The heterogeneous, fragmental structure of the stones with their chondrules presents the greatest discrepancy with such an origin. If we could show that the stones took on their present structure while under high pressure deep within a sizable mass or when it was disrupted, our difficulties in formulating a comprehensive and coherent explanation would be greatly diminished. Like the scientists of the past century, we shall remain at a stalemate unless we can penetrate and understand the structure of the stony meteorites.

We have compared the hypothetical parent of the meteorites with the earth and the other inner planets. When we examine these planets we find a most puzzling relation between density and size (Table 31). The moon has the density of ordinary silicates under

Table 31. *Diameter and density of moon and small planets.*

	Diameter (km)	Density (gm/cm³)
Moon	3,480	3.33
Mercury	5,000	3.8
Mars	6,770	3.96
Venus	12,400	4.86
Earth	12,700	5.52

low pressure and it can contain no appreciable quantity of dense metal as a core. Mercury and Mars may have small cores but whether they are metallic or are composed of dense compressed silicates is uncertain. The earth, however, has a sizable dense core and presumably Venus does also. If meteorites came from a planetlike body, it must have been comparable to the earth in size; otherwise it presumably would have had no core from which to produce metallic meteorites.

Meteorites seem to be fragments of one or more large bodies which we are also tempted to identify as the parents of the asteroids. Collision between two bodies of comparable mass, size, and structure is consistent with our limited evidence. If a body somewhat larger than Mars were struck at a velocity of about 1 kilometer per second by a body like Ceres or larger, much of the smaller body would probably be turned to gas, while the larger mass would be partially turned to gas but mainly shattered. A number of meteorites, both stony and metallic, show faults, cracks, and slip zones definitely of preatmospheric origin. Perry's careful and extensive study of metallic meteorites called attention to such faults and slip zones in the New Baltimore, Canyon Diablo from the Barringer Crater, and Helt Township meteorites (Plate 54). He further reminded us that the fine, scratchlike Neumann lines, found in many irons after etching, arose from slip or strain before the mass met the earth. Such features are to be expected if a solid parent mass was shattered by collision.

At the instant of collision part of the bodies would be turned to gas while other surface material, presumably of a stony composition, would be intensely heated. Perhaps such heating produced tectites and the black, glassy stones that comprise 3 percent of the stony falls.

Most of the fragments of such a collision would inherit orbital characteristics from their parents. Over considerable periods of time planetary perturbations would shuffle the orbits and possibly give rise to the currently observed distribution.

Collision between the many fragments will produce a further degrading of the particle sizes. Although we would expect the tougher irons to break often upon collision, they would not shatter to the same degree as the brittle stones. After collisions had occurred for a long interval of time, we would expect the earth to encounter more and smaller stony bodies than metallic. This is consistent with our observation that stony meteorites actually fall more frequently than metallic. We also note that the large meteor craters appear to have been formed by large metallic masses. To conclude that no large stony bodies exist between the planets would be unjustified, yet we wonder whether many of the larger asteroids may not be metallic. Further speculation along this line suggests that spectra may reveal nonshower meteors to be primarily stony material, although some of these meteors surely arise from cometary fragments too dispersed to be recognized as a meteor stream.

The discovery of several small asteroids moving in orbits similar to those of some fireballs demonstrates that the orbits of all these interplanetary bodies are interwoven; we are unable to distinguish a small asteroid from a large meteorite. To understand better the interplanetary material we must obtain all possible information from meteorites — our only laboratory material providing direct and extensive clues. Certainly much remains to be learned about these bodies.

☆

☆ **11** ☆

The Interplanetary Material

Between the visible stars the night sky is not black, but is faintly illuminated. Part of this light comes from faint stars, as in the Milky Way, and from starlight scattered by the atmosphere just as sunlight is scattered during the daytime. Modern spectrographic observations also show that over the sky there is a faint permanent aurora, or air glow. This seems to arise in the upper ionosphere some 250 kilometers above the earth. But a further component of this night skylight has quite different characteristics.

At the end of twilight a faint band of light can be seen stretching upward above the sun. This light, which is brightest along the ecliptic, is called the zodiacal light. It shows no sharp boundaries but, as Plates 65 and 66 show, fades off both perpendicularly to the ecliptic and with increasing angular distance from the sun. Visual, photographic, and photoelectric observations have traced it throughout the complete night sky. The contribution of the air glow to the night skylight can be separated from that of the zodiacal light because the air glow radiates a bright-line spectrum while the zodiacal light has the color of sunlight and a continuous spectrum like that of scattered sunlight.

From northern latitudes like those in the United States the zodiacal light is best seen when the ecliptic stands nearly vertical. This occurs in the evening during March and April and in the morning during September and October. At other times of the year the faint

172

cone of light lies more nearly along the horizon and may be obscured in the absorption and haze near the horizon. At the most favorable times of year the zodiacal light is about as bright as the Milky Way. Sometimes it is called the false dawn because it looks like the beginning of morning twilight even though the sun is still far below the horizon.

Just opposite the sun the faint skylight becomes more intense. There a large hazy area, termed the counterglow, 8° to 10° long and 5° to 7° wide, can be seen. The photoelectric observations of Behr and Siedentopf indicate that the counterglow exceeds the brightness of the nearby sky only by the equivalent of 30 stars of the tenth magnitude per square degree. While the zodiacal light can easily be seen at favorable times of the year, only the most keen-eyed observers detect the much fainter diffuse counterglow. The nature and origin of this faint light is not well understood. It may arise in part from a tail of atmospheric atoms pushed out behind the earth by solar radiation, or — and this seems more reasonable — it may be a phase-angle effect on sunlight reflected from interplanetary particles.

From the tropics, where the ecliptic always stands nearly vertical, the zodiacal light is quite conspicuous and readily observed throughout the year. Its brightness, measured photoelectrically in the ecliptic at a distance of 40° from the sun, is equal to five to ten stars of the fifth magnitude per square degree. This is 15 to 30 times the brightness of the counterglow.

The origin of the zodiacal light has long been a subject for speculation. It shows no parallax and seems to be as evanescent as a rainbow. Increasing observations of new types and growing information about the kinds and abundances of interplanetary materials are now pointing to a consistent and satisfactory answer.

There is general agreement that the zodiacal light arises from scattered sunlight. Between the planets there are several types of relatively abundant materials which may contribute to the total interplanetary illumination. Free electrons expelled from the sun and broken from interplanetary atoms and molecules by ultraviolet radiations are surely present. However, light scattered by free electrons is strongly polarized, whereas the zodiacal light shows a maximum of perhaps 20 percent polarization. If all of the polarized light is attributed to the presence of free electrons, they can account for not more than some 20 percent of the total brightness observed. That free electrons do contribute to the scattered light seems to be supported by observations that the zodiacal light becomes somewhat more concentrated toward the ecliptic at the times of minimum solar activity, when ionizing radiations from the sun are least intense.

Scattering by gas atoms and molecules is ruled out as a major contributor, for light scattered by them is strongly bluish, like skylight scattered by our atmosphere. Since the zodiacal light has the color of sunlight, gas atoms and molecules can play no major role as scattering agents.

Moving between the planets are numerous solid particles which produce meteors. From the numbers of meteors observed, the space density of these larger particles can be derived. Their number is far too small, by a factor of 1000 or even 10,000, to produce the observed brightness of the zodiacal light. Most of the light can, however, be attributed to scattering by tiny dust particles, meteor powder, only slightly larger than the wavelength of visible light. Such particles will scatter sunlight without coloring or polarizing it to an appreciable degree.

It therefore appears probable that the zodiacal light originates largely through the scattering of sunlight by an interplanetary mixture of free electrons and tiny dust particles. Since the light is concentrated along the ecliptic, these particles must be most abundant in that region of space. This we might have predicted, for the meteors and dust particles, arising from the distintegration of comets and perhaps from the fragmentation of asteroids when they collide, will be concentrated toward the plane of the ecliptic.

Both Allen and van de Hulst have suggested that the zodiacal light is an extension of the sun's outer corona. This outer corona, called the Fraunhofer corona and shown in Plate 67, has been observed out to several degrees from the sun's limb. Like the zodiacal light, the outer corona has the color and the continuous spectrum of sunlight. It is, however, closer to the sun and very much brighter than the zodiacal light. Careful photometric studies indicate, as Fig. 53 shows, that the decrease in brightness of the corona with increasing solar distance agrees well with the observed brightness of the zodiacal light at considerably greater solar distances. At the total eclipse in 1952 Jackson and Rense from an airplane observed the outer corona 9° from the sun. Their measure of the brightness at this distance from the sun fits well into the gap between the other observations of coronal and zodiacal light. We seem to be justified in concluding that these two phenomena arise from the same process.

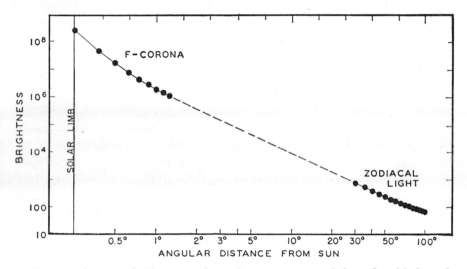

Fig. 53. *Change of brightness of the sun's outer corona and the zodiacal light with distance from the sun. (Courtesy of the* Astrophysical Journal.)

In this analysis the unknown quantities are the number and size of the interplanetary dust particles. That some exist is confirmed by the meteoritic dust and micrometeorites. For maximum scattering the particles needed are only a few wavelengths of light in diameter, that is, only a few microns across, and such particle sizes are assumed in the calculations. The calculated abundance of such particles needed to account for the observations seems reasonable. The interplanetary dust cloud is concentrated towad the ecliptic, but not as much so as the free electrons that produce the polarized light. Between the earth and the sun the density of dust seems to be fairly constant along the plane of the ecliptic, with perhaps a slightly lower density inside the orbit of Venus. The origin and stability of such a dust cloud must now receive our attention.

As we saw in the discussion of comets, the Poynting-Robertson effect acts to slow down small bodies moving around the sun and causes them to take on more nearly circular orbits and gradually spiral into the sun. This effect becomes increasingly selective for particles of smaller and smaller size. Whipple and Wyatt showed that in only 60 million years all particles smaller than 1 millimeter in diameter would be swept into the sun from as far out as the asteroidal zone. Furthermore, in 3000 million years particles with diameters as large as 8 centimeters would have been cleaned out of the same volume. Obviously we must search for some means of maintaining a steady supply of new dust particles.

From the calculated density of interplanetary dust particles of small size, Whipple found that close to a ton must be falling into the sun each second. As a possible source for such material he examined the wastage of the several comets that pass perihelion each year. All these comets probably release about as much material as did Halley's comet when it was at the earth's distance from the sun. This is 30 tons per second of dust, in addition to perhaps 100 tons per second of gases. Cometary wastage seems more than adequate to supply the number and size of particles needed.

Other sources may also contribute to the dust. Piotrowski investigated the amount of small material that may be released as the result of collisions between asteroids. Perhaps as much as 20 to 600 tons of material per second might be provided by such collisional crushing. Whether cometary material or asteroidal material is the principal source of the interplanetary scattering medium remains to be settled, but for once we have two mechanisms each of which appears to be more than adequate. Of the particles released in these manners, many will be influenced by perturbations and collisions with high-speed ionized material and perhaps ejected from the solar system. This wastage will reduce considerably the fraction of the raw material that as dust eventually spirals into the sun.

Other Points of View

Since we know the general way in which the interplanetary material is distributed, we may visualize how it would appear as seen from other planets, for example, Mercury, Mars, Jupiter, and Pluto. From atmosphereless Mercury, close to the sun, the zodiacal light would be much brighter than from the earth, and could be seen as a continuation of the sun's outer corona. Few comets would venture near and those that did would shoot past quickly. The asteroids would be faint, and many that we can observe from the earth would not be known. Because Mercury has little or no protecting atmosphere, meteorites must strike its surface with their full force, continually blasting craters ranging in size from pinpricks to gaping pits. As a result of their high speed near the sun and the lack of an air cushion, nearly all meteorites must be destroyed at impact.

The terrestrial astronomer transported to Mars would find the celestial scenery only slightly different in appearance. Perhaps the greatest change would be the decreased brightness of the zodiacal light, which would be very difficult to see. From Mars, almost in the asteroid zone, these little planets would be bright and easily observed. A few comets of large perihelion distance which remain too faint to be seen from the earth might be discovered. Rarely would a bright comet having a long tail be well placed for observation, because long tails grow only when a comet is near the sun; from Mars the majority would be lost against the bright sky of twilight. Numerous short-period comets pass inside the orbit of Mars, and meteor showers originating from them may be more numerous than on the earth. Sporadic meteors and meteorites may be more abundant but less conspicuous than those seen on the earth because their orbital velocities are lower.

From Jupiter our picture of the solar system, and especially of the interplanetary material, would be greatly changed. For example, the earth would never appear more than 11° from the sun — much closer than Mercury is to the sun as seen from the earth. The zodiacal light, comet tails, and other phenomena occurring near the sun would be practically unknown. Although a multitude of asteroids would be visible, they would not be as conspicuous as they would be from Mars, for when nearest they present their shadowed side to Jupiter. Just how Jupiter effects the capture of the short-period comets and how many of these move around the sun might be more apparent to the Jovian astronomer, for he would be at the source of the action and could watch it progress. Both sporadic meteors and meteor showers must appear frequently, owing as much to the great gravitational attraction of Jupiter as to its location far out in the interplanetary material.

From distant Pluto, nearly 40 times as far from the sun as we are on the earth, the interplanetary material would hardly be suspected. The zodiacal light and ordinary asteroids would be quite unknown. Comets passing nearby would be very faint bodies surrounded by perhaps a little dimly illuminated gas; at best they would be difficult to observe and relatively uninteresting.

In the Beginning

What part the interplanetary particles played in the origin and early history of the solar system we can only surmise. When we worry about how they, and the whole solar system, came into existence, we must not forget that the asteroids, comets, and meteors are interrelated. Moreover, we cannot neglect these millions of particles when discussing how the planets themselves were formed.

Throughout the preceding chapters we have tried to organize our knowledge of each type of interplanetary traveler and to see what type of origin might account for the observations. We might attempt to go even further, outlining how these processes could have arisen when the solar system was formed or in the intervening ages since. Such speculation hardly seems profitable, for we lack much essential information about each type of body in the system. Already we have many conflicting and contradictory conclusions to disentangle. Some of the contradictions may result from errors in our interpretation of the available observations, but they may also result from our incomplete and distorted information. On some subjects, like the motions of the asteroids, our knowledge is very precise; on other subjects it is sadly inaccurate.

Our general impression of the solar system is based on the majestic behavior of the planets. They are widely spaced and move in nearly circular orbits that change very slowly. The substructure of the system is entirely different. Here is a hurly-burly of perturbations, collisions, rapidly changing orbits, evaporation, and electrical influences. Where at first we tended to concentrate our attention on the motion and behavior of a particular few of these small objects, we now find statistical procedures necessary to describe the many variations and the average over-all state.

There is now a growing agreement that the meteorites probably came from the same source, or sources, as the asteroids. Most of the meteors photographed seem, by contrast, to have been released from comets. Either or both sources can supply the interplanetary dust that appears as micrometeorites and scatters the zodiacal light. Our problems seem to have been reduced in number, but this does not mean that they have been reduced in magnitude. Concerning each of the many types of bodies moving between the planets there is still much to learn.

APPENDIX

The Relation Between Solar Distance, Interval to Perihelion, and Temperature for Parabolic Orbits

In a parabolic orbit the interval t in days required for a body to move from a solar distance r in astronomical units to its perihelion at a solar distance q is given by the equation

$$t = 27.4(r + 2q)(r - q)^{\frac{1}{2}}.$$

The manner in which the temperature of a solid body will change with distance from the sun can be derived from two well-known relations. We assume that the body is a so-called "black body," which absorbs all the radiation falling on it, or a "gray body," which absorbs a fraction of the incident radiation, and reradiates a continuous spectrum appropriate to its temperature T. The solar energy E received per unit area by a body at solar distance r is inversely proportional to the square of the distance, that is, $E \sim 1/r^2$. This energy, according to Stefan's law, raises the body to a temperature T defined by the proportionality $E \sim T^4$. Upon eliminating E between these two relations, we have $T \sim 1/r^{\frac{1}{2}}$, or, more generally, $T_r = T_1/r^{\frac{1}{2}}$.

If the body is small or rotating rapidly, it will have at $r = 1$ a fairly uniform temperature throughout of about 4°C, or 277°K. If, however, it is large or keeps

Table A. Days to perihelion passage for parabolic orbits of different perihelion distances.

Absolute temperature (deg)		Solar distance, r (A.U.)	Perihelion distance, q (A.U.)						
$T_1 = 277$	$T_1 = 392$		0.0	0.2	0.4	0.6	0.8	1.0	1.2
196	277	2.0	77.5	88.1	97.1	103.8	108.0	109.6	107.8
206	292	1.8	66.1	76.2	84.3	90.0	93.2	93.0	88.6
219	310	1.6	56.1	64.8	72.0	76.7	78.2	76.0	69.4
234	331	1.4	45.4	54.0	60.3	63.6	63.4	59.0	46.6
253	358	1.2	36.0	43.9	48.9	50.7	48.5	38.0	0.0
277	392	1.0	27.4	34.3	38.0	38.2	31.9	0.0	
292	412	0.9	23.4	29.8	32.9	31.5	21.7		
310	438	.8	19.6	25.4	27.8	24.5	0.0		
331	468	.7	16.1	21.3	22.5	16.5			
358	506	.6	12.8	17.3	17.2	0.0			
392	554	.5	9.7	13.5	11.3				
438	620	.4	6.9	9.8	0.0				
505	720	.3	4.5	6.1					
620	875	.2	2.5	0.0					
886	1250	.1	0.9						

one side toward the sun for long intervals, the temperature of the illuminated side may rise to 119°C, or 392°K, while the dark side is very cold. These two values set the limits for the temperature of a solid atmosphereless body at the earth's distance from the sun.

The *total* interval at each perihelion passage during which a body is within a solar distance r, or while its temperature is above a specific temperature T, is twice the interval derived from the equation above and graphed in Figs. 3 and 4. Intervals to perihelion, or from perihelion, derived from this equation for various values of r and q are given in Table A, together with temperatures for the two extreme values of T_1 at $r = 1$ A.U.

INDEX

INDEX

PLATES

Plate 1. An asteroid trail. The asteroid reveals itself by moving during the 3-hr exposure. (Harvard College Observatory.)

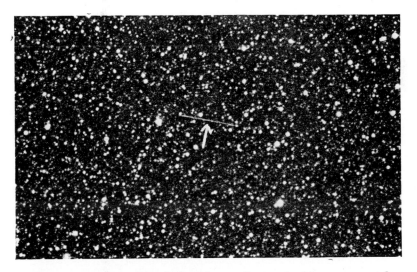

Plate 2. Discovery photograph of Icarus. During the 1-hr exposure, taken in 1949 by Baade with the 18-inch Schmidt camera on Mount Palomar, Icarus moved nearly 3′. (Mount Wilson and Palomar Observatories.)

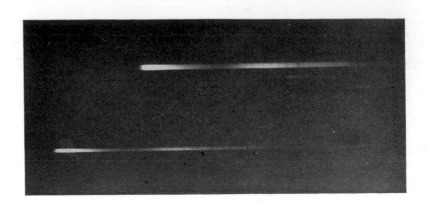

Plate 3. The light of Vesta and a star. The light of Vesta (above) has been dispersed by a prism, red on the left and photographed on a panchromatic film. Below is the spectrum of a star cooler and redder than the sun. The breaks in the middle of the spectra result from the relative insensitivity of the film to green light. (Harvard College Observatory.)

Plate 4. The variation of Eros. On January 28, 1938 Eros was moving southward rapidly and varying in brightness by more than one magnitude. Fifteen exposures, each of 6 min, show both the motion and the rapid fading of Eros. (Harvard College Observatory.)

Plate 5. *Halley's comet, May 6, 1910. Within the tail are many fine streamers and spikes. (Lick Observatory.)*

Plate 6. *Comet 1941 IV on February 19, 1941. This comet appeared in
the morning sky far south of the sun, then moved between the earth and the
sun and became briefly visible to the unaided eye from northern latitudes.
Its orbital motion quickly carried it away from the earth and the comet
faded rapidly. (Perkins Observatory.)*

Sept. 26   Oct. 24   Nov. 19

Dec. 4

Dec. 18   Dec. 25

Plate 7. The development of Cunningham's comet, 1941 I. When first discovered the comet was very small and faint. Early in December 1940 it began to develop a real tail and ceased to look like a pollywog. These six photographs are all on the same scale and had the same exposure times. (Harvard College Observatory.)

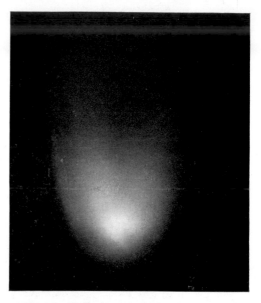

Plate 8. Halley's comet, May 5, 1910. Here the bright starlike nucleus is embedded within the diffuse asymmetric coma. (Lick Observatory.)

Plate 9. Halley's comet, May 8, 1910. Several envelopes or sharp gradations of light within the coma are visible. (Lick Observatory.)

Plate 10. Comet 1910 I. The tail of this bright comet consisted of several curved parts. The dark objects near the bottom of the picture are the outlines of trees blurred by the motion of the camera in following the comet. (Lowell Observatory.)

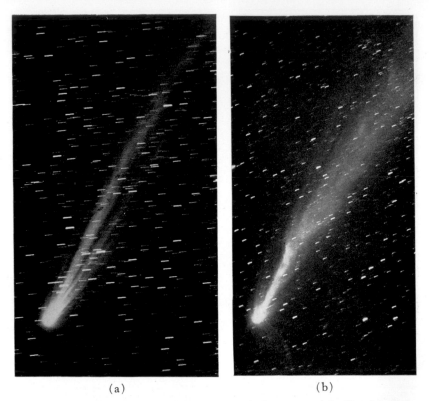

(a)   (b)

Plate 11. Variations in comet Morehouse: (a) the comet on October 23, 1908;
(b) a week later, October 30, 1908. (Harvard College Observatory.)

Plate 12. Rapid changes in comet Morehouse. On October 15, 1908, a
great cloud of gas shot out along the comet's tail. On the preceding night
the comet showed no indications that this great outburst was about to
occur. (Yerkes Observatory.)

Plate 13. Cunningham's comet, 1941 I, photographed on December 18–19, 1940, with lines of equal surface brightness derived by Watson from photographs exposed 1, 9, and 81 min. The entire pattern for the 1-min photograph fits inside the central isophote of the diagram above. The isophotes for the 9-min exposure are not shown. Magnitudes are based on an arbitrary zero point at the nucleus.

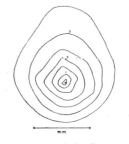

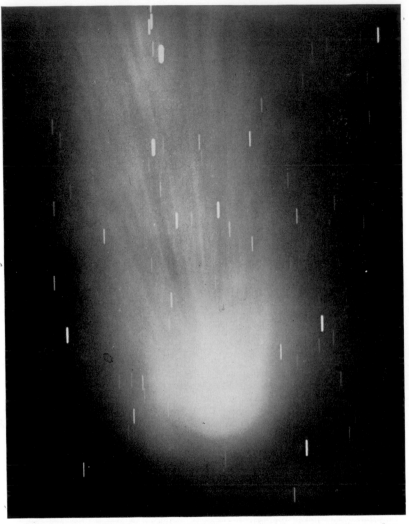

Plate 14. "A bagfull of nothing." Halley's comet on June 2, 1910 as photographed through the 60-inch telescope. (Mount Wilson Observatory.)

Plate 15. The spectrum of Cunningham's comet. The light of the comet was passed through a glass prism and photographed on a film sensitive to all radiations from violet to red. At various colors separate images of the comet appear. That on the left is caused by violet light from cyanogen, while those in the center are blue-green and greenish from carbon molecules. No strong images appear in the yellow and red light at the right. The band of light through the center is probably reflected sunlight. (Harvard College Observatory.)

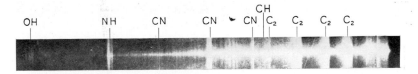

Plate 16. *Details of a comet's spectrum: the light of Cunningham's comet photographed through a slit spectrograph to show in detail the radiations of various molecules. The presence of OH and NH in a comet was discovered from this photograph by Elvey, Swings, and Babcock. (McDonald Observatory.)*

Plate 17. *A brilliant meteor photographed by accident on the edge of a plate being exposed to record the stars. (Harvard College Observatory.)*

Plate 18. A typical meteor photograph. The meteor first appears as a fine hairline, then brightens, fades, and ends in a final flash. (Harvard College Observatory.)

Plate 19. A multiple meteor camera and spectrograph. Millman used this mounting for two fast cameras and four spectrographs directed through the large rotating shutter. (Courtesy of Dr. Peter M. Millman.)

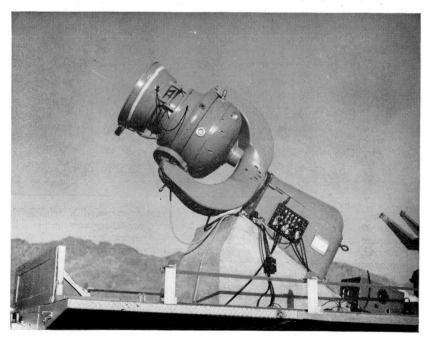

Plate 20. Baker-Super-Schmidt meteor camera. One of the cameras of focal ratio 0.67 and 55° field designed for the photography of faint meteors. (Perkin-Elmer Corporation.)

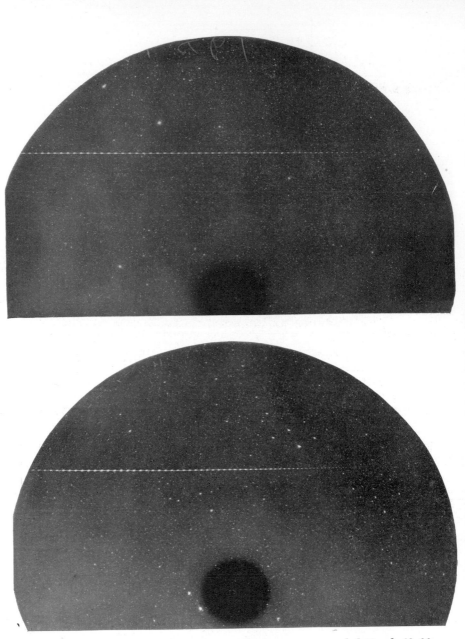

Plate 21. Duplicate photographs of a bright meteor recorded March 19–20, 1953 with super-Schmidt cameras in New Mexico. Over 60 segments are visible in each photograph, while the "breaks" between exposures, occurring 60 times a second, are partially filled by radiation from a lingering train. In the upper photograph the meteor passed near the handle of the Big Dipper. In the lower photograph, in which the stars have two images, the meteor passed near Corona Borealis. (Harvard College Observatory.)

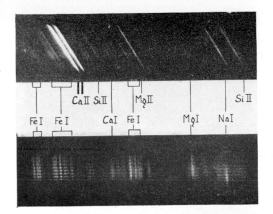

Plate 22. Spectra of two shower meteors. Above is the spectrum of a Perseid meteor, velocity 60 km/sec, photographed August 10, 1940. Radiations from both ions and neutral atoms are present. The violet radiations from calcium ions are the most intense. This spectrum is of type Y. Below is the spectrum of a Draconid meteor, velocity 23 km/sec, photographed October 9, 1946. Only radiations from neutral atoms are present. The spectrum is of type Z. Note that the yellow radiation from sodium, Na, begins after other lines appear and continues longer. Both spectra are enlarged from panchromatic films exposed through rotating shutters by P. M. Millman.

Plate 23. Seven sequential photographs of a meteor train recorded June 29–30, 1954 with a Super-Schmidt camera in New Mexico. The meteor moved from right to left and ended with a terminal flare. The drift of the train is apparent from its positions relative to the star images. The middle 5 exposures were of 2 sec duration; the first exposure was shorter and the last longer. (Harvard College Observatory.)

Plate 24. Long-enduring sunlit train of a meteor. This train in the wake of a bright meteor was visible for an hour and a half as it hung high above the earth in sunlight after twilight had fallen on the ground below. The train was 600 km from the photographer in Chicoutimi, Canada. (Photo by A. Stewart McNichols.)

Plate 25. The Leonid meteor shower of November 13, 1833, according to a contemporary artist.

Plate 26. Photograph of Draconid trails, October 9, 1946, made by K. Spain and Carl K. Seyfert, at Vanderbilt University. The original plate recorded 38 Draconid meteors during the single 12-min exposure. The radiant point is just out of the picture in the upper right-hand corner. Stars in Cygnus appear across the center of the picture, while Vega is to the right. (Vanderbilt University.)

Plate 27. A bright Geminid meteor. This meteor was so bright it cast shadows. It progressed from left to right, passing north of the Pleiades near the center of the picture, and split as it neared the end of its path. (Harvard College Observatory.)

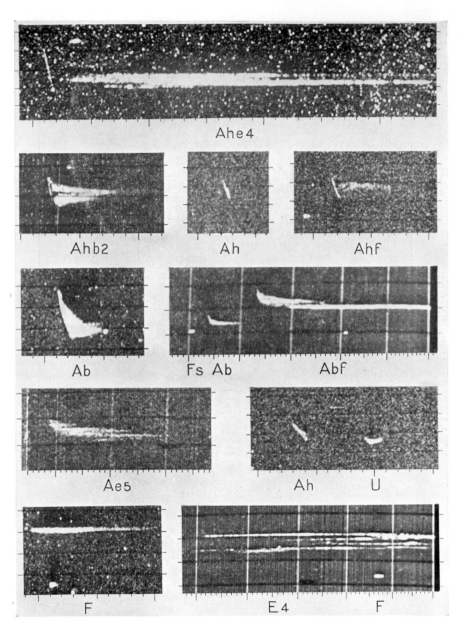

Plate 28. Types of radar meteor echoes recorded with 10-meter radar and a range-time display. The horizontal time scale is graduated in 1-sec intervals, with later time at the right. The vertical scale is graduated in 20-km intervals. These records define part of a provisional classification system. The "head echo" h, at the left in the upper record, is followed over 1 sec later by an enduring train having four components at different ranges. (Canadian National Research Council.)

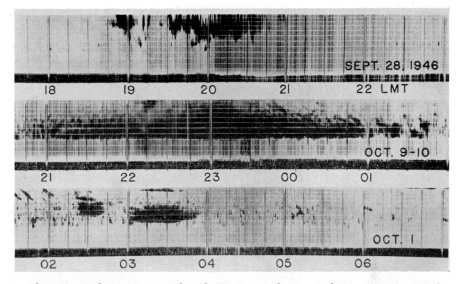

Plate 29. *Reflections received with 86-meter radar waves by J. A. Pierce. At the top are reflections from the aurora borealis. The central pattern was obtained during the Draconid meteor shower of October 9, 1946. The patches of ionization produced by over 4000 meteors became so numerous that they formed a nearly continuous reflecting layer at a height of 90 km. The lower strip, for a fairly typical night, shows two large clouds of sporadic E-layer ionization and numerous individual meteor echoes. (J. A. Pierce, Harvard University.)*

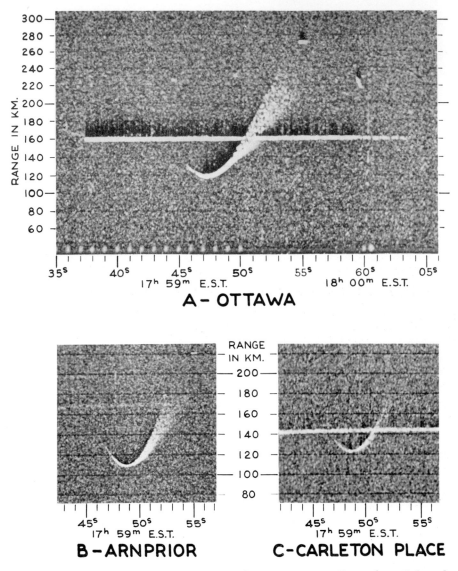

Plate 30. Three simultaneous radar records of one meteor. From these J-shaped records McKinley and Millman derived the path, velocity, and orbit of this meteor. In the background is an enduring echo which had a real height of 100 km and drifted southward at 20 km/hr. (Canadian National Research Council.)

Plate 31. The Plainview meteorite from Texas. These two stones, found a half mile apart, fit together perfectly. (Photo by H. H. Nininger.)

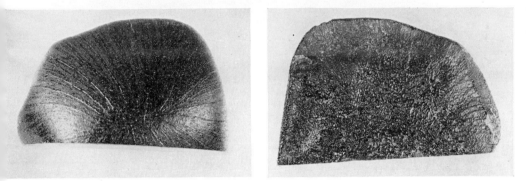

Plate 32. Flow marks on the Lafayette meteorite. The liquid glassy crust formed during the air flight spread out from a single point. Little crust formed on the back, shown at the right. Part of the meteorite has been cut off. (U. S. National Museum.)

Plate 33. Excavation of the Hugoton, Kansas meteorite. This stony meteorite, weighing 346 kg, was discovered by J. O. Lynch, Jr., when a plow turned up a fragment. When excavated by Nininger, it proved to be one of the largest stony meteorites known. (Photo by H. H. Nininger.)

Plate 34. A metallic meteorite, weighing over 130 kg, unearthed by La Paz in 1939. It was found at a depth of 1 meter after being located by use of an electric "divining rod." (Photo by Lincoln La Paz.)

Plate 35. *This collection of 13 metallic meteorites was unearthed at the Odessa meteor crater after La Paz had surveyed the region for only 12 hr using the meteorite detector of the Ohio State University meteorite expedition of 1939. (Lincoln La Paz.)*

Plate 36. *The Hoba West meteorite, largest known. This 60-ton mass of metal lies where it was found in South-West Africa. (L. J. Spencer.)*

Plate 37. The Ahnighito meteorite, largest in captivity. The late Dr. Clyde Fisher examining the meteorite, which was found in Greenland and brought to New York by Peary in 1897. (Thane L. Bierwert, American Museum of Natural History, New York.)

Plate 38. The Willamette meteorite. Its present weight is 14 tons, but before the deep pits were formed the weight must have been near 25 tons. (Julius Kirschner and Clyde Fisher, American Museum of Natural History, New York.)

Plate 39. The Barringer meteor crater, Arizona. The great crater, more than 1 km wide, photographed from the north at an altitude of 2000 feet. (Photo by Clyde Fisher.)

Plate 40. The west rim of the Barringer Crater. This photograph shows the sharply upturned rocks in the rim and the great quantity of fragmental material lying about. (Lincoln La Paz.)

Plate 42. The New Quebec (Chubb) Crater photographed from an altitude of 20,000 feet by the Royal Canadian Air Force. The circular form of the crater contrasts with the finger lakes of this recently glaciated region. From the lines of snow in gullies around the crater, the high upturned crater rim can be visualized. (Photo copyright by National Geographic Society.)

Plate 43. The main crater at Henbury, Australia, 200 meters long and 110 meters wide, the largest of a group of 13 meteor craters. (Photo by A. R. Alder man, from the Mineralogical Magazine.)

Plate 41. The southeast section of the wall of the Barringer meteor crater as seen from the crater floor. To the left center are uptilted strata, while to the right is the great arch raised vertically. Presumably the meteorite burrowed under this arch. (Photo by C. A. Federer.)

Plate 44. The Wolf Creek Crater in Australia, which is over 800 meters wide and 60 meters deep; it has an upturned rim up to 30 meters high. (The Australian Geographical Society.)

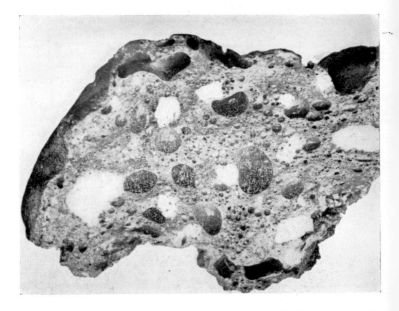

Plate 45. Silica glass from Wabar, Arabia. The broken surface of a silica bomb shows patches of white glass and large bubbles embedded in gray and blue glass. This silica foam contains many minute spherules of shiny nickel-iron. (Photo from the Mineralogical Magazine.)

Plate 46. The footprint of a meteorite. Reinwaldt examining the funnel-shaped depression he found under a small meteor crater on the Oesel Islands in the Baltic Sea. (Photo by Clyde Fisher.)

Plate 47. Destruction near the Tunguska meteor craters. Over an area nearly 100 km across, the trees were pushed over by the great blast of hot air that shot out when the meteor struck the earth.

Plate 48. The rim of the Barringer meteor crater. Seen from a distance of several kilometers the crater resembles the numerous craters on the moon. (Photo by Clyde Fisher.)

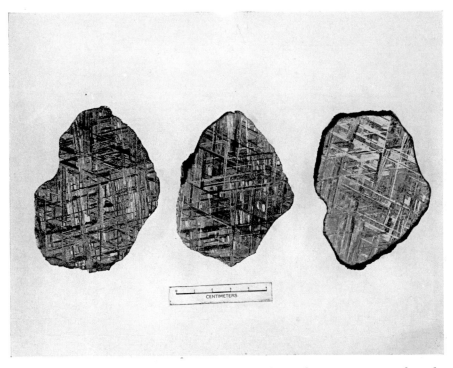

Plate 49. The Hill City meteorite, a fine octahedrite. These cross sections show the Widmanstätten bands extending to the outer surface of the mass. Because the kamacite bands are thin, the specimen is classified as a fine octahedrite. It contains 9.21 percent of nickel. (U. S. National Museum.)

Plate 50. The Odessa meteorite, a coarse octahedrite. This body is unusually rich in the typical inclusions found in metallic meteorites. It illustrates the difficulties of selecting samples that will give representative chemical compositions. The smaller bodies within the kamacite are iron carbide — cohenite. The larger rounder inclusions are iron sulfide — troilite — of which many are darkened by free carbon. Nearly every troilite inclusion is surrounded by iron-nickel phosphide — schreibersite. The irregular and angular inclusions are also schreibersite. All these inclusions separated from the iron and nickel matrix at relatively high temperatures. (U. S. National Museum.)

Plate 51. Enlarged section of the Grant meteorite, a medium octahedrite. The gray lamellae are kamacite, the thin lines bounding them are taenite, and the dark enclosed areas are plessite. These are the three important iron and nickel components of metallic meteorites. The granular band in the center is a plate, or lamella, of schreibersite. The roundish dark areas in opposing corners are troilite inclusions. The lack of perfection within many metallic meteorites is well illustrated by this specimen. (U. S. National Museum.)

Plate 52. *Internal structure of the Wood's Mountain meteorite. Magnified 83 times, this octahedrite shows wide bands of granulated kamacite bounded by narrow taenite bands. The black areas are plessite, having varied appearance and structure. (Stuart H. Perry.)*

Plate 54. Section of a Bethany meteorite. This meteorite, one of more than 50 found close together in South Africa, shows several sets of Widmanstätten figures. Each marks a single crystal that existed in the meteorite when it had a temperature near 1000°C. (Harvard Geological Museum.)

Plate 53. The Mayodan meteorite, a hexahedrite. This meteorite, of low nickel content, is essentially pure cubic kamacite with inclusions of troilite. The lines intersecting at right angles are cleavage directions in the kamacite, for this polished surface is parallel to one face of the cubic crystal structure. The fine lines, like scratches, known as Neumann lines, were formed by a heavy blow. (U. S. National Museum.)

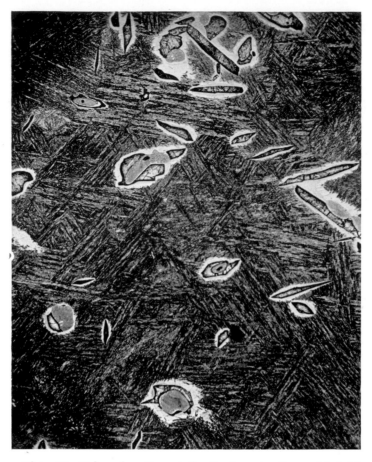

Plate 55. Enlarged section of the Freda meteorite, a nickel-rich ataxite. This meteorite, 23.5 percent nickel, shows no Widmanstätten pattern. Abundant inclusions of kamacite surrounded by shiny areas of taenite occur throughout the mass. Many of the kamacite inclusions surround bodies of iron phosphide. (U. S. National Museum.)

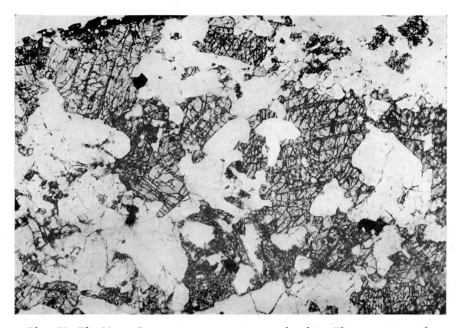

Plate 56. The Moore County stony meteorite, an achondrite. The meteorites without chondrules, called achondrites, resemble terrestrial rocks more closely than do any other class of stony meteorites. The light areas here are feldspar, while the dark areas are pyroxene surrounding parallel lamellae of augite. This meteorite is practically free of metallic inclusions. (U. S. National Museum.)

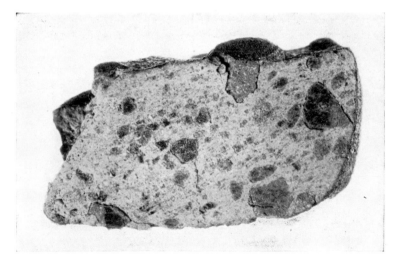

Plate 57. Cross section of the Pasamonte stony meteorite, an achondrite. This meteorite is rich in calcium but free of chondrules, although it contains many irregular nodules. (U. S. National Museum.)

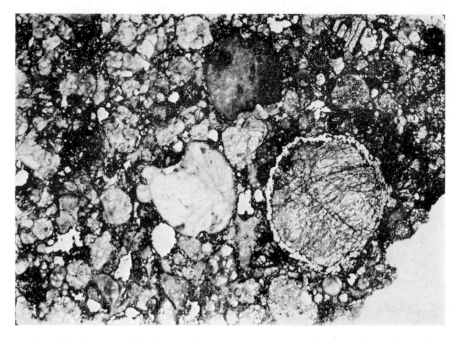

Plate 58. Section of the Tennasilm stony meteorite, a chondrite. Several complete chondrules of different sizes are seen in a matrix of smaller and partly crushed chondrules. The dark material is glassy, while the white areas are metal. A metallic halo encloses one chondrule, but metal seldom occurs within chondrules. (U. S. National Museum.)

Plate 59. Cross section of the Cumberland Falls stony meteorite. This meteorite, which fell in Kentucky on April 9, 1919, consists of two materials differing greatly in appearance. (U. S. National Museum.)

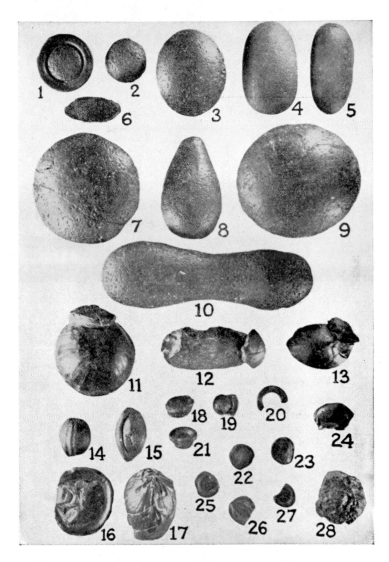

Plate 60. Typical tectites, part of the Kennett Collection from Australia studied by Charles Fenner of the University of Adelaide. This group, 0.8 times natural size, illustrates the variety of shapes customarily found among tectites, ranging from flanged buttons (1) through oval forms to teardrops (8) and dumbbells (10).

Plate 61. *A slice of the Brenham meteorite, a stony-iron. The dark areas are olivine, a dense silicate, enclosed in metallic iron. The sizable mass of metal shows a fine octahedral pattern. Because the metallic mesh seems to be continuous, the meteorite is classed as a pallasite. (U. S. National Museum.)*

Plate 62. *The Crab Orchard meteorite, a stony-iron. This body consists of granular aggregates of metal and silicates. The two large metallic areas show well-developed Widmanstätten figures. Small metallic inclusions throughout the mass appear as whitish areas. The dark, angular areas are silicates free from metal. This meteorite is classified as a mesosiderite. (U. S. National Museum.)*

Plate 63. The Carlton meteorite, a fine octahedrite. This beautiful meteorite shows irregular, angular inclusions of schreibersite surrounded by swathing kamacite. (U. S. National Museum.)

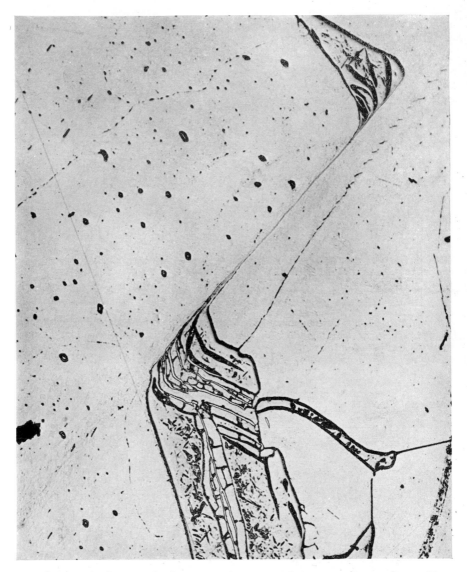

Plate 64. Evidence of displacement. The tip of a plessite area in a Canyon Diablo meteorite from the Barringer Crater has been sheared off by displacement, leaving a connecting thread of taenite. (U. S. National Museum.)

Plate 65. The zodiacal light, as painted by E. L. Trouvelot on February 20, 1876. The sharp boundaries depicted here are not confirmed by photographic or photoelectric observations. (Courtesy of The Sky Publishing Corporation.)

Plate 66. *Photograph of the zodiacal light, stretching upward as a diffuse cone of light above the sun. The photograph was made on October 12, 1950 by Sharpless and Osterbrock at the Yerkes Observatory with a special wide-angle camera designed by Greenstein and Henyey. The three dark lines are shadows of the supports holding the photographic plate.* (Reproduced by permission of the Astrophysical Journal.)

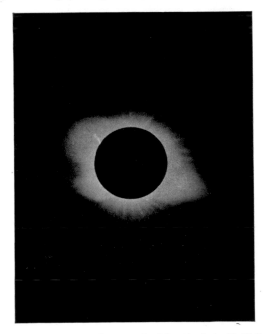

Plate 67. *The sun's corona photographed by Paul A. McNally during the eclipse of 1932. Between the long coronal streamers can be seen the brighter part of the outer Fraunhofer corona.* (© National Geographic Society, 1932. By special permission.)